TOBIRA I: Beginning Japanese Workbook 1
−Hiragana/Katakana, Kanji, Reading, Writing

First published 2022

Kurosio Publishers
4-3, Nibancho, Chiyoda-ku, Tokyo 102-0084, Japan

ISBN 978-4-87424-910-9
Printed in Japan

TOBIRA
BEGINNING
JAPANESE

初級日本語
とびら
I

ワークブック❶
ひらがな・カタカナ｜かんじ｜よむ｜かく

WORKBOOK 1
Hiragana | Katakana | Kanji | Reading | Writing

[著者] 岡まゆみ　　近藤純子　　榊原芳美　　西村裕代　　[監修] 筒井通雄
Mayumi Oka　　Junko Kondo　　Yoshimi Sakakibara　　Hiroyo Nishimura　　Michio Tsutsui

Kurosio Publishers

はじめに

本書は『初級日本語 とびらI』で学んだひらがな・カタカナ・漢字を強化すると共に、日本語を読む力と書く力を身につけるためのワークブックです。本書には学習者が各練習で学習のポイントを理解し、楽しく効率的に勉強できるよう様々な工夫が施してあります。主な特徴は次の通りです。

- 正しくきれいな字が書けるように、注意点が分かりやすく提示されている。

- 単調になりがちな仮名・漢字の練習を楽しく行うことができる。

- 字形・字音・字義を意識させる多様な練習問題で、漢字の読み方や形を覚えるだけでなく、意味や用法も確認しながら学習することができる。

- 楽しく、バラエティに富んだ練習問題を通して、様々な漢字学習の方法を知ることができる。

- 文字の練習では難易度が3段階で示されており、段階的に学習することができる。

- 「読む練習」では文構造の把握から内容理解まで、正確により深く読む力が身につく。

- 「書く練習」では本書独自のワークシートを活用することで、自分で考えて自分の言葉で情報や考えを伝える力が身につく。

- 「各課のとびら」や練習問題を通して、日本の文化や言語景観についても知ることができる。

- 二色刷りで紙面が見やすく、文字練習の注意点やポイントも分かりやすい。イラストや写真も豊富。

本書は授業での練習、宿題や小テスト、復習、自主学習用の練習として使うことができます。難しいと感じたところや苦手なところは繰り返し練習することをおすすめします。

本書制作にあたり、緻密で的確な校閲・校正をしてくださった平川ワイター永子さんには大いに助けられ、それにより本書の質を向上させることができました。また、ロビン・グリフィンさんには適切な英語翻訳と校正をしていただきました。お二人のご尽力に改めてお礼申し上げます。

最後に、くろしお出版編集部の市川麻里子さんと金髙浩子さんには本書の制作全般にわたって大変お世話になりました。お二人の目配りの行き届いた校閲・校正と優れた編集のおかげで、学習者の興味とやる気を引き出す紙面にすることができました。いつも迅速に、かつ忍耐強く、我々の意向に応え、対応していただいたことに深く感謝申し上げます。

2022年9月

著者一同

CONTENTS

How to use this workbook
このワークブックの使い方

The following is an overview of the organization and contents of this workbook.

このワークブックは次のような構成と内容になっています。

■ How to write Japanese characters

This section covers fundamentals to know before writing Japanese characters for the first time, including how to follow stroke order and other points of note. Be sure to read this section before proceeding to the lessons in this workbook.

■ How to write Japanese characters

ここでは、日本語の文字を練習する前に知っておくと役に立つ基本的な知識や、文字を書く時の一般的な注意事項を説明しています。また、文字の書き順などの説明もありますから、各課の練習に入る前に必ず読んでください。

■ Structure of each lesson

| 各課のとびら Lesson preview | → | ひらがな／カタカナ／かんじのれんしゅう Hiragana / Katakana / Kanji practice | → | よむれんしゅう Reading practice | → | かくれんしゅう Writing practice |

■ 各課の構成

| 各課のとびら Lesson preview | → | ひらがな／カタカナ／かんじのれんしゅう Hiragana / Katakana / Kanji practice | → | よむれんしゅう Reading practice | → | かくれんしゅう Writing practice |

■ Lesson preview

- This page introduces the characters to be practiced in the given lesson, as well as activities, fun graphics, and more. Before moving on to the practice problems, check out this page for a preview of the characters you'll be studying.
- Lessons with Kanji practice sections (Lessons 3-10) include both an Entry Check and Exit Check. Before starting the Kanji practice problems for a given lesson, use the Entry Check to mark which kanji you know how to read and write (○), which you recognize but cannot yet read and write (△), and which you don't know at all (×). After completing the practice problems for that lesson, use the Exit Check to confirm whether you have learned those kanji. Mark those you can now read and write, and review practice problems for unlearned kanji as needed.

■ 各課のとびら

- 各課で導入する内容に関係した楽しい情報や各課で学ぶ漢字が実際に使われている画像などがあります。練習を始める前に、まず各課でどんな文字を学ぶか見てみましょう。
- 漢字練習の課（L3〜L10）には Entry Check と Exit Check があります。Entry Check は各漢字の練習を始める前に、その漢字を読んで書くことができたら○、どちらか一方だけだったら△、全然知らなかったら×を入れます。その課の練習が全部終わったら、Exit Check で練習した漢字がマスターできたかどうかをチェックします。読み書きともにできるようになっていたら○を入れてください。できていなければその漢字をもう一度練習しましょう。

■ Hiragana and katakana practice [Lessons 0-2]

- First, use the boxes to practice writing characters. The dashed guiding lines will help you write more balanced characters. Each character is shown with a stroke order, arrows marking line directions and angles, starting points and other notes to pay attention to. Refer to "How to practice writing characters in this workbook" (**3** on p.8) for an overview of the notation used in this workbook. After practicing tracing and writing the characters in the boxes, proceed to the practice problems to test your recognition of the characters. Problems include selecting proper stroke order and character form, identifying mistakes, distinguishing

■ ひらがなとカタカナの練習 [Lessons 0-2]

- まず、マス目で文字を練習しましょう。補助線に沿って書くと、文字をバランスよく書くことができます。各文字には、筆順、線の角度や方向を示す矢印、注意点及び各画の始点が表示されています。p.8 の **3** How to practice writing characters in this workbook を参照し、丁寧に練習していきましょう。文字練習の後には、文字認識の練習が続きます。筆順や字形を問う問題、間違い探し、類似文字を区別する問題などを通して、それぞれの文字の形を正しく理解できているか、確認しましょう。

between similar characters, and other tasks designed to help you better understand the correct form of each character.

- Having learned the characters, the next task is to write words that contain them. The majority of these words can be found in *TOBIRA I: Beginning Japanese* (hereafter *TOBIRA I*). Each word is shown with an illustration and English translation so its meaning can be readily understood. You will practice writing these words both horizontally and vertically. (See 🄸 on p.9, "Horizontal writing and vertical writing.")

- Katakana practice problems feature commonly used katakana words, as well as those grouped into categories like IT terminology and country names. Some exercises include instructions to read each word aloud. Reading the words while listening to how they sound leads to more effective learning comprehension. Use the sounds, written characters, and illustrations together to learn katakana in a more holistic, word-level approach.

■ Kanji practice [Lessons 3-10]

Kanji practice for each lesson begins with learning how to write each character introduced, then moves to reading the characters in context.

- In practicing character form, trace the gray guiding lines while following the given stroke order and stroke types (stop, flick, etc.).
- Then, using the model as a guide, write the kanji twice as neatly as possible in the two empty boxes. If you need more practice, use a notebook or separate sheet of paper to continue writing each character.
- Next, proceed to reading and writing practice problems for that lesson's kanji.

The difficulty of each practice problem is marked with a number of ★ s:

★ = basic
★★ = sentence-level
★★★ = practical application

Practice problems include opportunities to solve kanji puzzles, break down the elements that make up each kanji, learn and provide *okurigana*, work with "The Story of Kanji" sections of the main textbook, and other ways to put what you've learned into practice. These exercises cover not just new kanji from that lesson, but also past lessons' kanji for better repetition and retention. Finally, the end of the lesson moves beyond just reading and writing each character, providing a space to practice writing full sentences while using kanji in context.

- 文字をマスターしたら、実際のことばを文字で書く練習をします。ここで練習するひらがなとカタカナのことばは『初級日本語 とびらⅠ』(以下、『とびらⅠ』) に出てくるものがほとんどです。全てのことばには、意味がすぐに理解できるようイラストや英訳が付いています。また、横書き・縦書きの両方が練習できるようになっています (p.9 🄸 Horizontal writing and vertical writing 参照)。

- カタカナ練習には身近なカタカナ語や、IT 関係・国名などカテゴリー別にまとめたカタカナ語が出てきます。Read aloud と指示がある練習問題では、そのことばを声に出して言ってみましょう。目で見て読み、耳で聞くと、学習効果は倍増します。音と文字、そして絵のイメージをリンクさせ、カタカナを一字ずつの音だけでなく、単語レベルで覚えるようにしましょう。

■ 漢字の練習 [Lessons 3-10]

各課の漢字の練習は字形の練習から始まり、漢字の読み書きの練習へと続きます。

- まず、字形練習は、漢字の書き順やトメ、ハネなどを見ながらグレーの線をなぞります。
- 次に、手本の漢字を見ながら、できる限り丁寧にバランスが整った漢字を二回書きます。ここでは二回だけ書くことになっていますが、ノートなど他の紙に何度も練習するといいでしょう。
- 最後に、漢字を読んだり書いたりする練習をします。

各問にある★の数は難易度を表します。

★ = 基本練習
★★ = 文レベルの練習
★★★ = 応用練習

漢字の練習にはクイズのような楽しい練習、漢字を構成する部首や正しい送りがなを学ぶ練習、『とびらⅠ』の「かんじのはなし」に関連した練習など、様々な問題形式があるので、楽しく練習できます。また、その課の新しい漢字だけでなく、既習の漢字も問題に入っているので、それらを繰り返し練習できます。最後は漢字を使って文を書く練習があり、漢字だけを単に「読む・書く」練習だけでなく、漢字を「文脈の中で使う」練習もできるようになっています。

■ Reading practice [Lessons 1-10]

Reading practice corresponds to the "Reading" segments of *TOBIRA 1* (intensive reading). These segments feature engaging topics for a content-based learning approach. Read the passages from the main textbook, then write your answers in your workbook. If you run out of space, use the margins or a separate piece of paper. Note that there is no answer section for "Understanding Japanese sentence structure" questions in this workbook; for these tasks, write your answers in your textbook as you read through the text.

■ Writing practice [Lessons 1-10]

Writing practice provides a space to practice writing full compositions while expanding on content presented in Reading practice. First, use the "Pre-writing activity" worksheet to collect your thoughts and organize information. Using this worksheet will give your ideas more clarity, allowing you to write more cohesive essays. Then, using the grammar, vocabulary, and kanji learned for that lesson, draft your essay from your outline. Presenting your finished essay in class or posting it on social media are great ways to share your ideas with others. Writing sheets are available for download via the Workbook section on the *TOBIRA* website below.

■ Columns

This workbook also features columns that cover topics like punctuation marks, writing names, and kanji elements, as well as examples of Japanese handwriting.

■ Answer sheets

Answers can be written in and submitted directly from the workbook, though the same answer sheets are available for download via the Workbook section on the *TOBIRA* website below.

■ 読む練習 [Lessons 1-10]

読む練習には『とびらⅠ』「よみましょう」のセクション2(精読)の質問の部分が載っています。教科書の読み物を読んで、このページに解答を書き込んでください。解答スペースが狭い場合は、余白に書き込んだり別紙を使ったりしましょう。文型把握の問題(Understanding Japaense sentence structure)には解答欄がありません。この問題の答えは、本文を読みながら教科書に書き込んでください。どれも学習意欲を促す知的でおもしろい読み物なので、楽しんで読んでください。

■ 書く練習 [Lessons 1-10]

書く練習は読む練習の内容を発展させた活動で、身近な話題についてまとまりのある文章を書く練習です。まず Pre-writing activity のワークシートを使って考えや情報を整理し、書く内容を準備してください。このワークシートを使用することで、何を書くかが明確になり、まとまりのある文を無理なく書くことができます。その後で、その課で習った文法や単語、漢字を使いながら、ワークシートにまとめたことを書きましょう。書けたら、是非クラス内で発表したり SNS で発信したりして、色々な人と共有してください。書く練習の解答用紙は下の「とびら初級 WEB サイト」の「ワークブックエリア」からダウンロードすることができます。

■ コラム

句読点の使い方、名前の書き方、漢字の部首についての説明、そして、手書き文字の例があるので、参考にしてください。

■ 解答用紙について

解答用紙は本書に書き込んで切り取って提出することができますが、下の「とびら初級 WEB サイト」の「ワークブックエリア」からダウンロードすることもできます。

tobirabeginning.9640.jp/workbook/

■ Answer keys

Instructors can access answer keys by registering through the Instructor Resources section on the *TOBIRA* website. An electronic version can otherwise be purchased and viewed separately.

■ 解答について

解答は「とびら初級 WEB サイト」の「教師エリア」に登録するとご覧になれます。登録教師以外の方は別売の電子版をご覧ください。

How to write Japanese characters

Nyanta

Tobira-sensee, the three types of Japanese characters, hiragana, katakana, and kanji seem hard to learn!

Don't worry! If you follow the guidelines in this workbook step by step, you'll definitely learn how to read and write them easily and correctly.

Tobira-sensee

The goal of this pre-lesson is to learn useful tips for writing Japanese characters. Some hiragana characters are used as examples, but it's okay if you don't know how to read them yet.

■ When writing characters

① Use a pencil with an eraser so you can easily fix mistakes. If you want to use a tablet and stylus, it's best to have a brush stroke feature enabled.

② Note how you hold your pencil. Hold your pencil as shown in the illustration.

correct way   wrong way

The dynamic tripod grasp: hold the pencil with your thumb and index finger about an inch from its tip, with your middle finger supporting the pencil.

② Basic strokes

Japanese characters consist of simple lines and dots, commonly called "strokes." If you get used to writing the strokes below, it'll be easier to learn Japanese characters.

① Strokes: lines

Horizontal	Vertical	Diagonal	Curved	Bent
—	│	／ ＼	( )	〈 〉 フ ㄱ

② Strokes: dots and a small circle

Vertical dot	Diagonal dots	Double dots	Small circle

*The double dots and the small circle are called diacritical marks.

③ Stroke-endings

Stop: The stroke ends with a full stop.	Release: The stroke ends with the tip of the pencil being gradually lifted.	Flick: The stroke ends with a flick.

Practice writing each of the lines, dots, and stroke-endings. Trace the gray lines and dots first, then rewrite them in the blank boxes on the right. Practice more using your notebook or tablet if necessary.

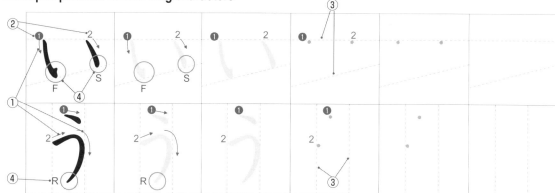

❸ How to practice writing characters in this workbook

When writing Japanese characters, pay attention to points ①-④ below.

◆ Example: practice handwriting characters

① Stroke direction

The general rule is that characters are written from left to right and from top to bottom. Curved lines bend at varying angles. In this workbook, directions and angles of strokes are shown with red arrows. (See ④ for more details.)

② Stroke order

Each character is written in a pre-determined stroke order. By following this stroke order, you can write more neatly, make fewer mistakes, and memorize the characters more easily. In this workbook, the stroke order for each character is shown using Arabic numerals. The number ❶ indicates the first stroke.

③ Guiding lines

All writing exercises include dashed guiding lines for writing more balanced characters. Using these lines will allow you to write cleaner, more correct characters.

④ Abbreviation codes and symbols

The following abbreviation codes are used to indicate the correct way to write characters.

S = stop   F = flick   R = release   C = curved line   ↓→ = direction   ◯ = note   ◌ = space

4 Horizontal writing and vertical writing

Japanese can be written both horizontally and vertically. You will learn the rules and features of each style in L8 (p.293) of *TOBIRA I*. In this workbook, you will practice writing horizontally and vertically as in the examples below.

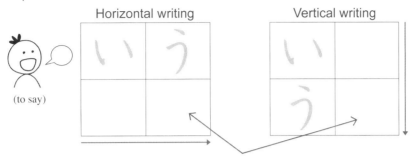

Practice writing in these blank boxes.

5 Differences between handwritten and printed characters

Both handwritten and printed characters are introduced in *TOBIRA I* (p.11). When you practice writing characters, use the handwritten styles, not the printed styles. The examples below show some of the distinct differences between handwritten and printed characters. (Different parts are indicated with ◯.)

| Mincho font | Gothic font | Handwritten | | Mincho font | Gothic font | Handwritten |

Tobira-sensee, I can just type characters on my computer, tablet, etc., so why do I have to practice writing characters by hand?

First, handwriting helps to improve both focus and memory. Particularly when learning kanji, handwriting the characters makes them easier to memorize!

Handwriting can be time-saving and convenient in some situations, too. In fact, there are many situations where you have to write by hand. For example, when filling out paperwork at a city hall or hospital, jotting down memos or spoken messages, writing your name and answers on a test, etc.

It's also good to note that there's an artistic appreciation for handwriting and calligraphy in Japan, so being able to skillfully write these characters will help make a good impression.

As you can see, there is much to be enjoyed through handwriting these characters, and I hope this workbook is a great resource for you!

Hiragana List できる**Check** ☑

In the chart below, each hiragana is shown with an illustration of a word that contains it. Most highlighted hiragana are at the start of the word, but some are not. After learning all hiragana, come back to this chart to see if you can read and write all characters.

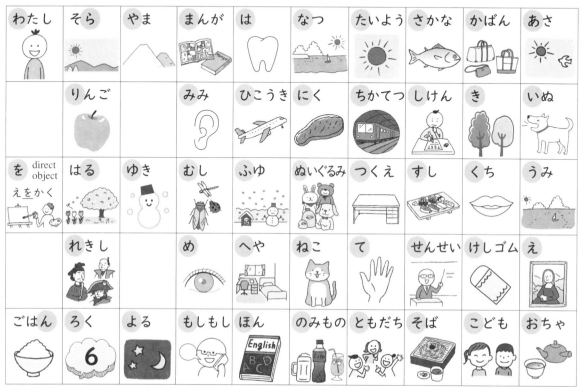

Sing a song and learn hiragana!

Below are the lyrics to *A-I-U-E-O no Uta* (The A-I-U-E-O Song), which can be sung to the tune of *Twinkle Twinkle Little Star*.

ひらがなのれんしゅう | Hiragana practice

★1 Trace the gray hiragana first, then write each hiragana as neatly as you can in the boxes below.

S = stop F = flick R = release C = curved line ↓ → = direction

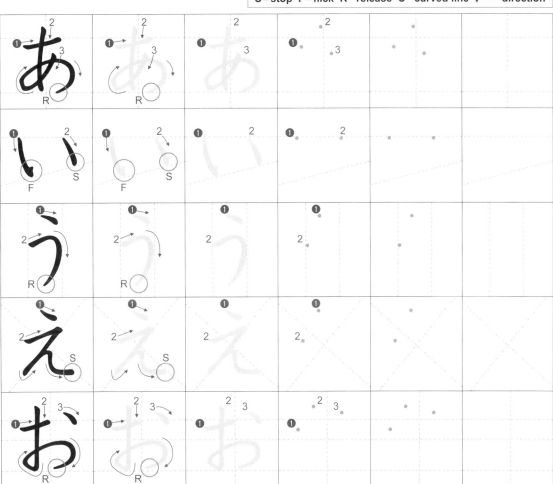

★2 Circle the indicated stroke in each hiragana as in the example.

Ex. — 2nd
1) — 1st
2) — 2nd
3) — 3rd

★3 For each hiragana, mark the correct one with a ✓, then circle the mistake(s) in the other ones.

Ex. あ ✓
1) い
2) う
3) え
4) お

11

4 Trace the gray hiragana first, then rewrite each word in the space provided. Write horizontally or vertically, following the arrow.

1) (love)

2) (above)

3) (blue)

4) (picture)

5) (a lot)

6) (I see!)

7) (no)

5 Convert each romanized word into hiragana in the space provided. Write horizontally or vertically, following the arrow.

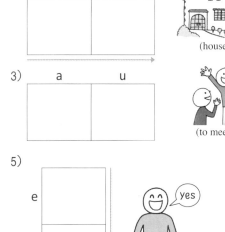

1) i e (house)

2) o u (king)

3) a u (to meet)

4) o o (Oh!)

5) e / e (yes)

6) i / u (to say)

ひらがなのれんしゅう │ Hiragana practice

★1 Trace the gray hiragana first, then write each hiragana as neatly as you can in the boxes below.

S=stop F=flick R=release C=curved line ↓→=direction

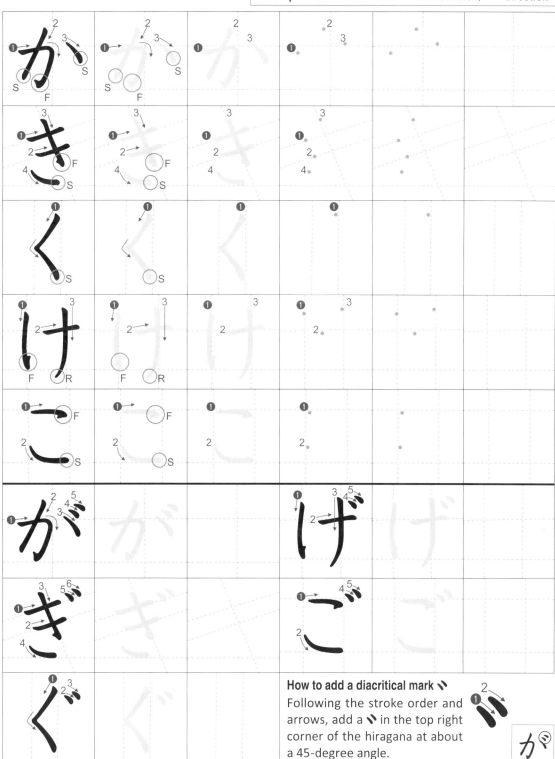

How to add a diacritical mark ＼＼
Following the stroke order and arrows, add a ＼＼ in the top right corner of the hiragana at about a 45-degree angle.

13

2 Circle the indicated stroke in each hiragana as in the example.

3 For each hiragana, mark the correct one with a ✓, then circle the mistake(s) in the other ones.

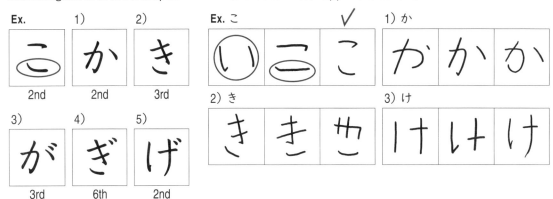

4 Trace the gray hiragana first, then rewrite each word in the space provided, following the arrow.

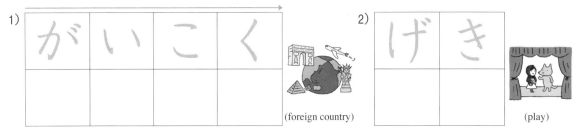

1) がいこく (foreign country)

2) げき (play)

5 Convert each romanized word into hiragana in the space provided. Write horizontally or vertically, following the arrow.

1) a ki (autumn)

2) ke ga (injury)

3) ka gu (furniture)

4) go go (afternoon)

5) (train station) e ki

6) (pond) i ke

7) (key) ka gi

8) (to write) ka ku

9) (to listen to) ki ku

Class: _____ Name: _____

ひらがなのれんしゅう｜Hiragana practice

① Trace the gray hiragana first, then write each hiragana as neatly as you can in the boxes below.

S=stop F=flick R=release C=curved line ↓→=direction

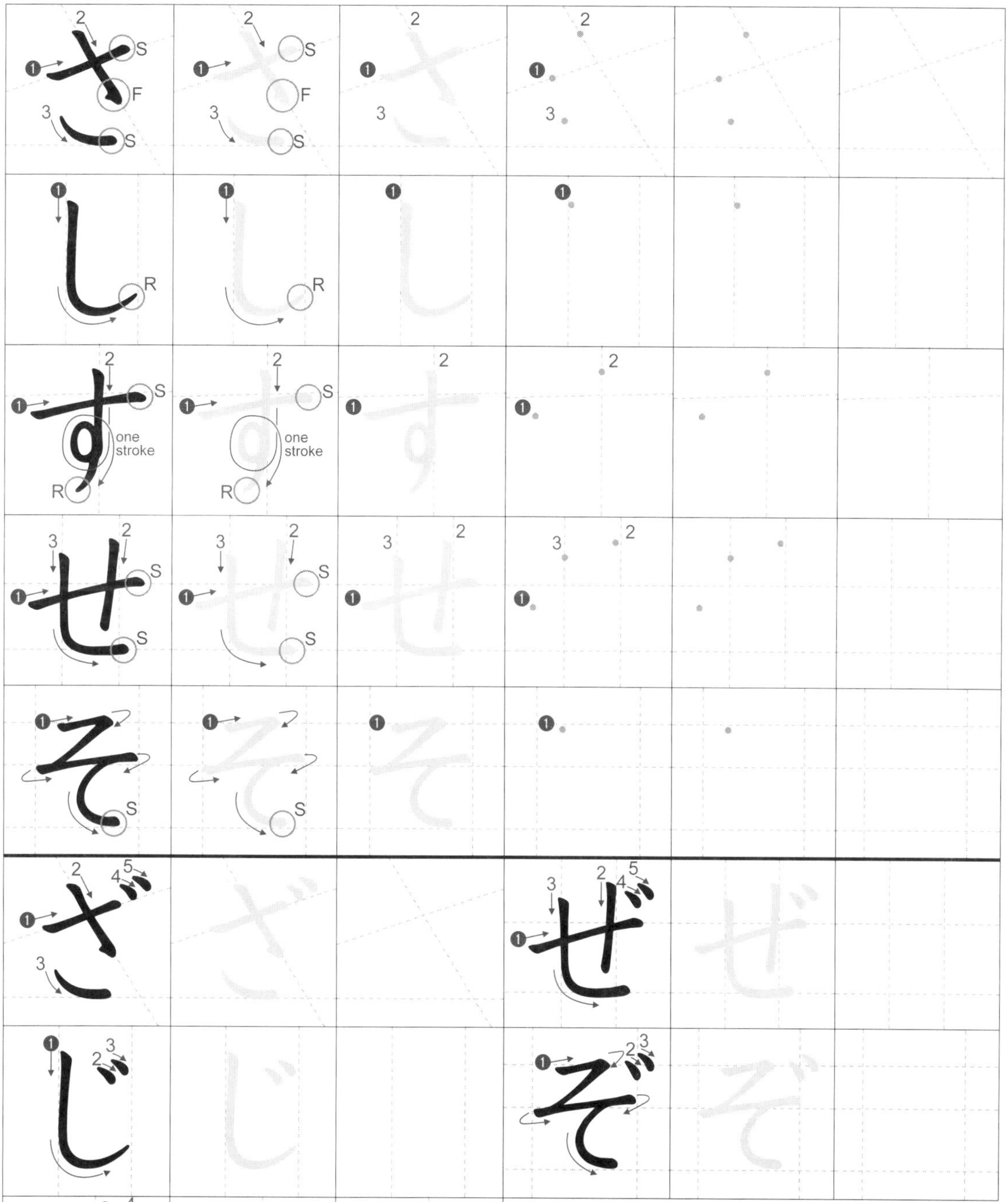

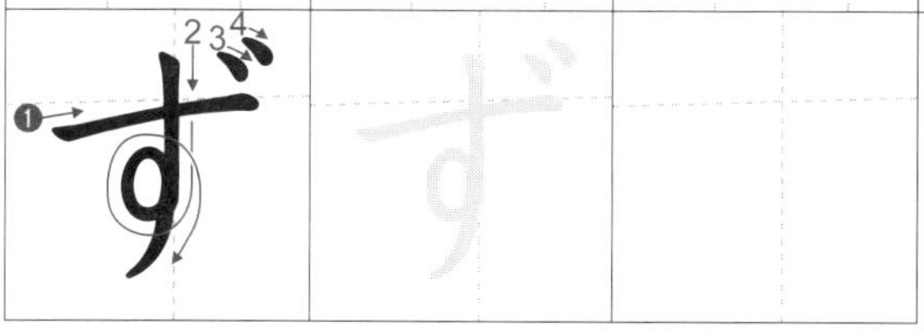

さ

し

す

せ

そ

ざ　　　　　　　ぜ

じ　　　　　　　ぞ

ず

Insert a diacritical mark ゛ for each hiragana in the appropriate place at the correct angle.

さ　し　す　せ　そ

② Circle the indicated stroke in each hiragana.

1) す
2nd

2) さ
2nd

3) せ
1st

4) じ
2nd

③ For each hiragana, mark the correct one with a ✓, then circle the mistake(s) in the other one(s).

1) さ

2) し

3) す

4) せ

5) そ

6) じ

④ Trace the gray hiragana first, then rewrite each word in the space provided. Write horizontally or vertically, following the arrow.

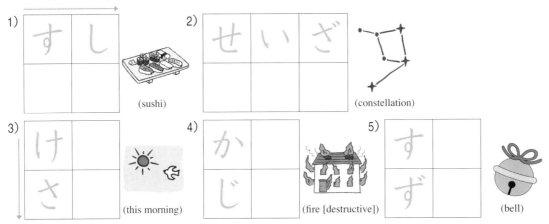

1) す し
(sushi)

2) せ い ざ
(constellation)

3) け さ
(this morning)

4) か じ
(fire [destructive])

5) す ず
(bell)

⑤ Convert each romanized word into hiragana in the space provided. Write horizontally or vertically, following the arrow.

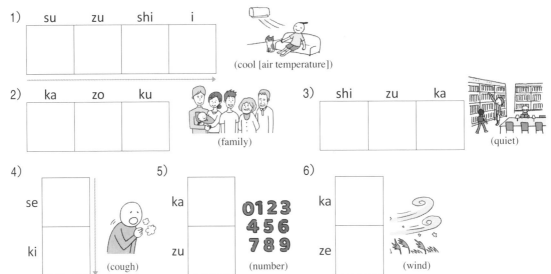

1) su zu shi i
(cool [air temperature])

2) ka zo ku
(family)

3) shi zu ka
(quiet)

4) se ki
(cough)

5) ka zu
(number)

6) ka ze
(wind)

ひらがなのれんしゅう｜Hiragana practice

⭐1 Trace the gray hiragana first, then write each hiragana as neatly as you can in the boxes below.

S=stop F=flick R=release C=curved line ↓→=direction

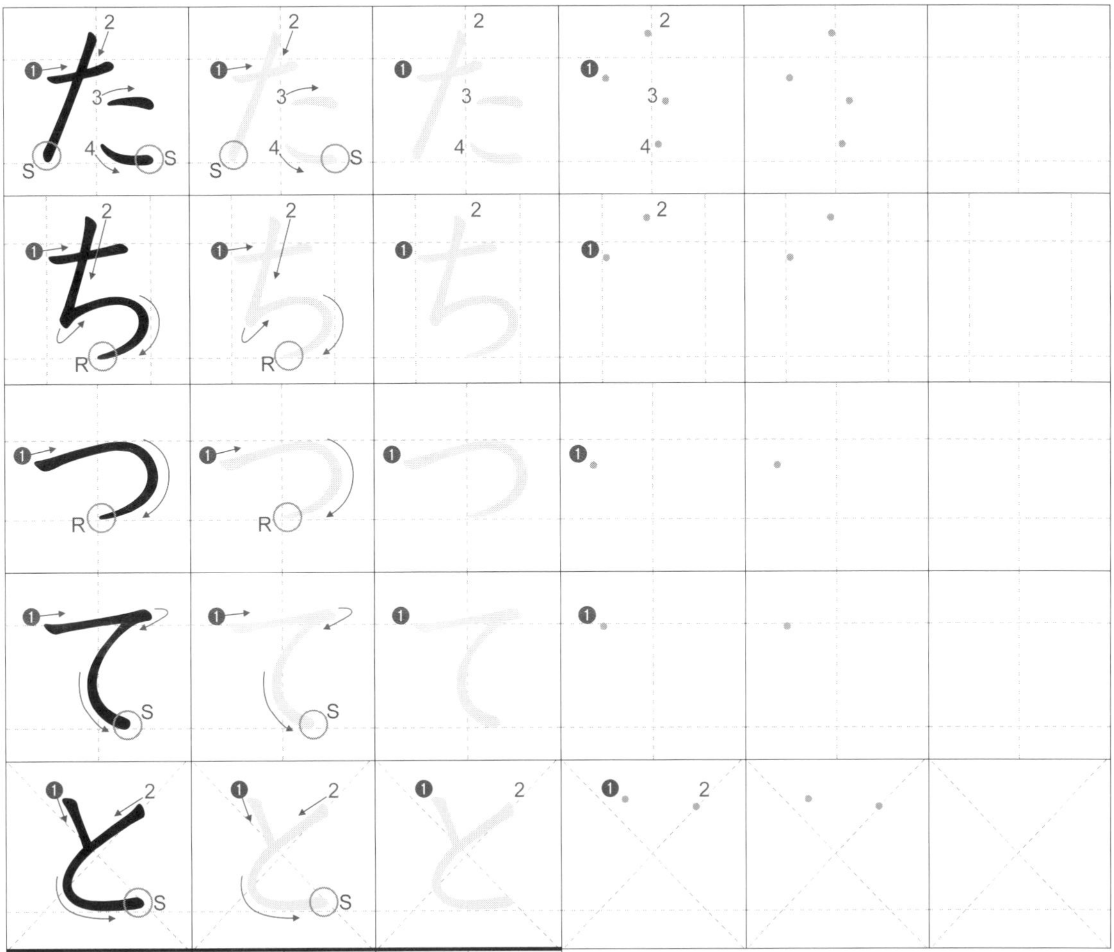

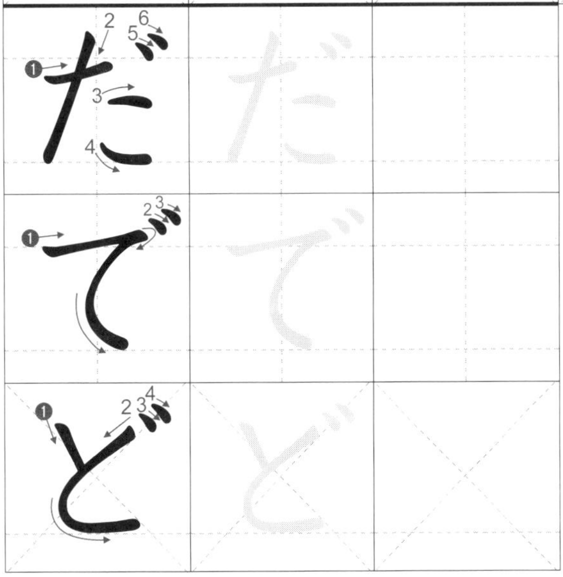

た

ち

つ

て

と

だ

で

ど

Choose the correct direction for the diacritical mark.

a.　　b.　　c.　　d.

17

★2 Circle the indicated stroke in each hiragana.

1)
た
2nd

2)
ち
1st

3)
で
2nd

4)
と
1st

★3 For each hiragana, mark the correct one with a √, then circle the mistake(s) in the other one(s).

1) た
た　た　た

2) ち
ち　ち　ち

3) つ
つ　つ　フ

4) て
て　て

5) と
と　と

★4 Trace the gray hiragana first, then rewrite each word in the space provided. Write horizontally or vertically, following the arrow.

1)
ついたち

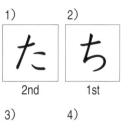
(the first day of the month)

2)
であう

(to encounter)

3)
ときどき

(sometimes)

4)
ちず

(map)

5)
ち
ち

(father)

6)
た
だ

(free of charge)

7)
つ
き

(the Moon)

★5 Convert each romanized word into hiragana in the space provided, following the arrow.

1) te tsu da u

(to help)

2) chi ka te tsu

(subway)

3) ta tsu

(to stand up)

4) da i ga ku

(university)

ひらがなのれんしゅう│Hiragana practice

★1 Trace the gray hiragana first, then write each hiragana as neatly as you can in the boxes below.

S = stop F = flick R = release C = curved line ↓ → = direction

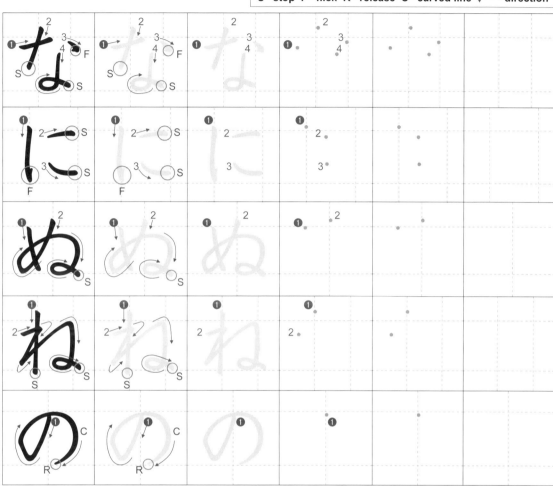

★2 Circle the indicated stroke in each hiragana.

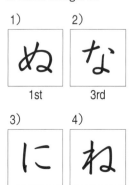

1) ぬ — 1st
2) な — 3rd
3) に — 2nd
4) ね — 1st

★3 For each hiragana, mark the correct one with a ✓, then circle the mistake(s) in the other ones.

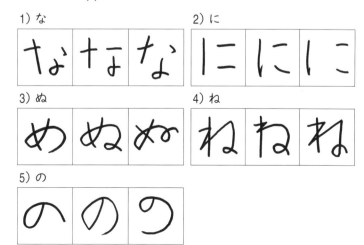

1) な
2) に
3) ぬ
4) ね
5) の

4 Trace the gray hiragana first, then rewrite each word in the space provided. Write horizontally or vertically, following the arrow.

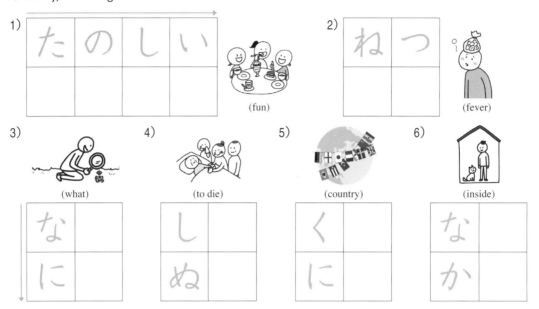

1) たのしい (fun)

2) ねつ (fever)

3) (what) なに

4) (to die) しぬ

5) (country) くに

6) (inside) なか

5 Convert each romanized word into hiragana in the space provided. Write horizontally or vertically, following the arrow.

1) sa ka na (fish)

2) ni ku (meat)

3) o ka ne (money)

4) no do (throat)

5) ni ga tsu (February)

6) na ku (to cry)

7) a ni (older brother) (older sister) a ne

8) nu gu (to take off)

9) na tsu (summer)

10) ta ne (seed)

11) nu u (to sew)

ひらがなのれんしゅう | Hiragana practice

★1 Trace the gray hiragana first, then write each hiragana as neatly as you can in the boxes below.

S=stop F=flick R=release C=curved line ↓→=direction

は は は は

ひ ひ ひ ひ

ふ ふ ふ ふ

へ へ へ へ

ほ ほ ほ ほ

ば ば ば ぱ ぱ

び び ぴ ぴ

ぶ ぶ ぷ ぷ

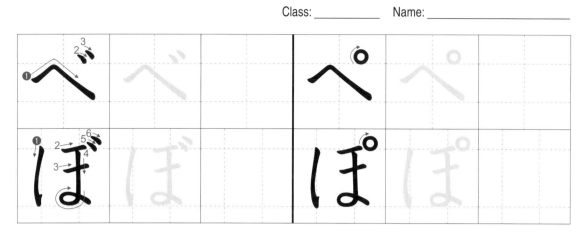

★2 For each hiragana, mark the correct one with a ✓, then circle the mistake(s) in the other one.

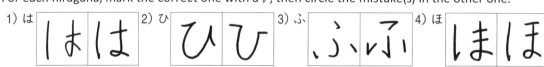

1) は   2) ひ   3) ふ   4) ほ

★3 Trace the gray hiragana first, then rewrite each word in the space provided, following the arrow.

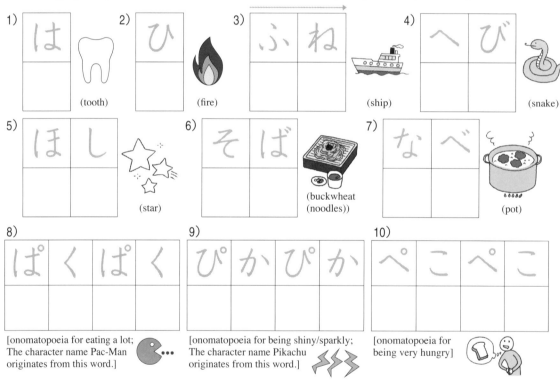

1) は (tooth)   2) ひ (fire)   3) ふね (ship)   4) へび (snake)

5) ほし (star)   6) そば (buckwheat (noodles))   7) なべ (pot)

8) ぱくぱく
[onomatopoeia for eating a lot; The character name Pac-Man originates from this word.]

9) ぴかぴか
[onomatopoeia for being shiny/sparkly; The character name Pikachu originates from this word.]

10) ぺこぺこ
[onomatopoeia for being very hungry]

★4 Convert each romanized word into hiragana in the space provided, following the arrow.

1) ha / ha (mother)

2) so / fu (grandfather)   so / bo (grandmother)

3) to / bu (to fly)

ひらがなのれんしゅう │ Hiragana practice

1 Trace the gray hiragana first, then write each hiragana as neatly as you can in the boxes below.

S = stop F = flick R = release C = curved line ↓ → = direction

ま	ま	ま			
み	み	み			
む	む	む			
め	め	め			
も	も	も			
や	や	や			
ゆ	ゆ	ゆ			
よ	よ	よ			

★2 For each hiragana, mark the correct one with a ✓, then circle the mistake(s) in the other one.

1) ま ｜ ま ｜ ま

2) み ｜ み ｜ み

3) む ｜ む ｜ む

4) め ｜ め ｜ め

5) も ｜ も ｜ も

6) よ ｜ よ ｜ よ

7) や ｜ や ｜ や

8) ゆ ｜ ゆ ｜ ゆ

★3 Trace the gray hiragana first, then rewrite each word in the space provided. Write horizontally or vertically, following the arrow.

1) み み
(ear)

2) い も う と
(younger sister)

3) (mountain) や ま

4) (insect) む し

5) (snow) ゆ き

6) (often) よ く

★4 Convert each romanized word into hiragana in the space provided, following the arrow.

1) u mi
(sea)

2) ma do
(window)

3) he ya
(room)

4) yu me
(dream)

5) to mo da chi
(friend)

6) mi zu
(water)

7) a me
(rain)

8) yo mu
(to read)

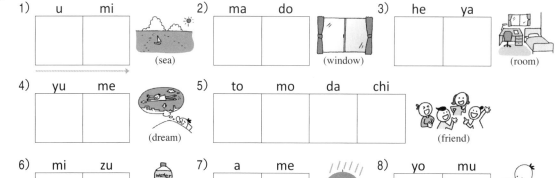
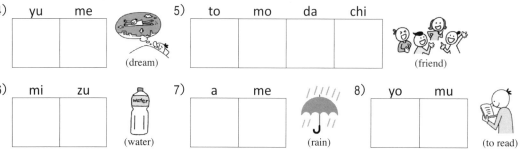

ひらがなのれんしゅう | Hiragana practice

1 Trace the gray hiragana first, then write each hiragana as neatly as you can in the boxes below.

S = stop F = flick R = release C = curved line ↓ → = direction

2 For each hiragana, mark the correct one with a ✓, then circle the mistake(s) in the other one.

1) ら

2) り

3) る

4) れ

5) ろ

6) わ

7) を

8) ん

3 Trace the gray hiragana first, then rewrite each word in the space provided. Write horizontally or vertically, following the arrow.

1) りんご
(apple)

2) さ ら を わ る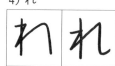
(plate)
(to shatter)
⌐ the direct object marker

3) れ き し
(history)

4) 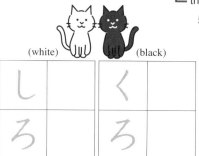 し ろ / く ろ
(white) (black)

5) み ん な
(everyone)

4 Convert each romanized word into hiragana in the space provided. Write horizontally or vertically, following the arrow.

1) go ha n
(cooked rice)

2) ku su ri
(medicine)

3) ha re ru
(to clear up)

4) wa ta shi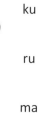
(I)

5) ku ru ma
(car)

6) o te ra
(temple)

れんしゅう | Practice

★1 Review: Hiragana

⒈ Circle the hiragana that represents the romanized sound.

Ex. a ［あ・め］　1) ki ［き・さ］　2) chi ［ち・ら］　3) ni ［た・に］　4) nu ［ね・ぬ］

5) ho ［は・ほ］　6) me ［ぬ・め］　7) ri ［い・り］　8) ro ［ろ・る］　9) wa ［れ・わ］

⒉ Write the hiragana that represent the romanized sounds below as neatly as you can.

Ex. e ___え___　1) ke _____　2) su _____　3) so _____　4) na _____

5) fu _____　6) ma _____　7) mu _____　8) yu _____　9) n _____

★2 Practice: Long vowels (See pp.25-26 in *TOBIRA I*.)

For each vowel, trace the gray hiragana first and rewrite the word in the space provided below. Then, convert the romanized words into hiragana.

aa	おかあさん (mother)	obaasan (grandmother)	aa (I see!)	waa (Wow!)
ii	おにいさん (older brother)	ojiisan (grandfather)	chiisai (small)	kiiro (yellow)
uu	すうがく (math)	taifuu (tyhoon)	kuuki (air)	jiyuu (freedom)
ee	えいご (English)	sensee (teacher)	gakusee (student)	tokee (watch)
	おねえさん (older sister)	ee (yes)	hee [interjection to show your surprise and interest]	
oo	おとうさん (father)	otooto (younger brother)	imooto (younger sister)	doozo (please)
	おおきい (big)	koori (ice)	ooi (a lot)	tooi (far)

★
3 Practice: Double consonants (small っ)

1 Match the romanized sentences to the ones in hiragana in the box on the right. Pay attention to the differences between the three sentences.

1) Kittekudasai   2) Kitekudasai   3) Kiitekudasai

(Please cut.)

(Please come (here).)

(Please listen.)

(　) きいてください

(　) きてください

(　) きってください

2 Trace the gray hiragana first, then rewrite each word in the space provided. Write horizontally or vertically, following the arrow. Pay attention to the position and size of small っ.

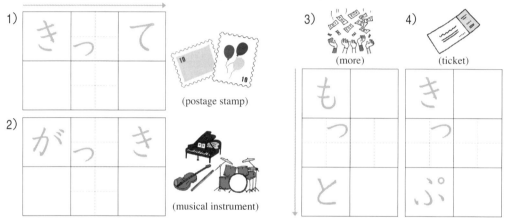

1) きって
(postage stamp)

2) がっき
(musical instrument)

3) もっと
(more)

4) きっぷ
(ticket)

3 Provide hiragana for each romanized word in the space provided. Write horizontally or vertically, following the arrow.

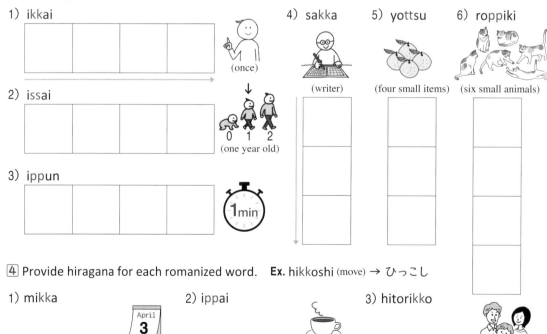

1) ikkai
(once)

2) issai
(one year old)

3) ippun
(1min)

4) sakka
(writer)

5) yottsu
(four small items)

6) roppiki
(six small animals)

4 Provide hiragana for each romanized word. **Ex.** hikkoshi (move) → ひっこし

1) mikka
April **3**
_____ (the third day)

2) ippai
_____ (one cup of ...)

3) hitorikko
_____ (only child)

★
④ Practice: Contracted sounds (small や, ゆ, and よ)

Lessons
0&1

☐ Trace the gray hiragana first, then rewrite each word in the space provided. Write horizontally or vertically, following the arrow. Pay attention to the position and size of small や, ゆ, and よ.

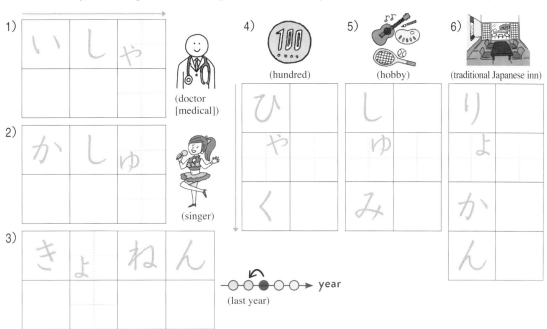

1) いしゃ (doctor [medical])
2) かしゅ (singer)
3) きょねん (last year)
4) ひゃく (hundred)
5) しゅみ (hobby)
6) りょかん (traditional Japanese inn)

☐ Provide hiragana for each romanized word in the space provided. Write horizontally or vertically, following the arrow.

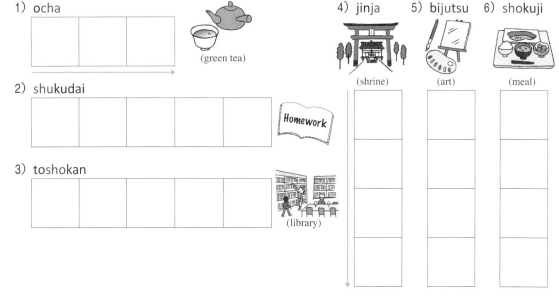

1) ocha (green tea)
2) shukudai (Homework)
3) toshokan (library)
4) jinja (shrine)
5) bijutsu (art)
6) shokuji (meal)

③ Provide hiragana for each romanized word. Ex. shashin (photograph) → しゃしん

1) jitensha (bicycle) _____
2) sanbyaku (three hundred) _____
3) omocha (toy) _____

29

★⑤ Practice writing words containing long vowels, double consonants, and contracted sounds.

[1] Trace the gray hiragana first, then rewrite each word in the space provided. Write horizontally or vertically, following the arrow.

1)

2)

3) (today)

4) (if that's the case) / (nine)

5) (meow) / (week) / (dormitory)

6)

[2] Trace the gray hiragana first, then rewrite each word in the space provided. Write horizontally or vertically, following the arrow.

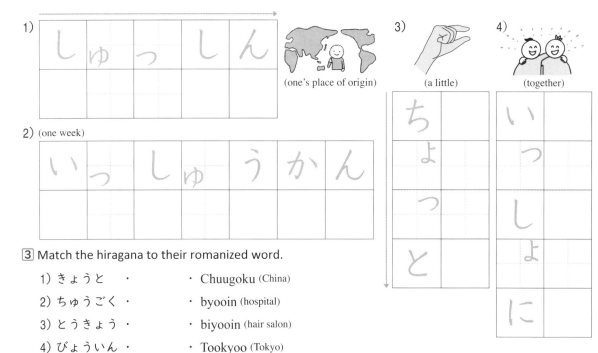

1) (one's place of origin)

2) (one week)

3) (a little)

4) (together)

[3] Match the hiragana to their romanized word.

1) きょうと   ・   ・ Chuugoku (China)

2) ちゅうごく ・   ・ byooin (hospital)

3) とうきょう ・   ・ biyooin (hair salon)

4) びょういん ・   ・ Tookyoo (Tokyo)

5) びよういん ・   ・ Kyooto (Kyoto)

★★ 6 Practice writing with all the special sounds. Provide hiragana for each romanized word.

1 School

1) jugyoo
(class)

_____

2) benkyoo
(study)

_____

3) shusseki
(attendance)

_____

4) seeseki
(grade
(on a test, etc.))

_____

5) kyookasho
(textbook)

_____

6) gakki
(semester)

_____

7) shokudoo
(cafeteria; dining hall)

_____

8) renshuu
(practice)

_____

2 Places in town

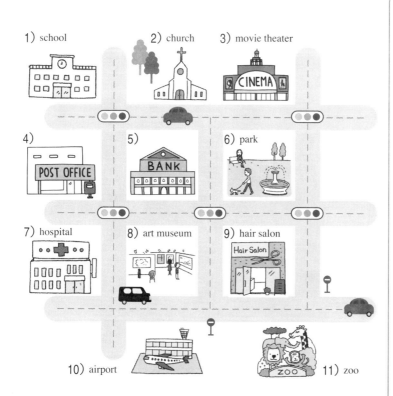

1) school
2) church
3) movie theater
4) POST OFFICE
5) BANK
6) park
7) hospital
8) art museum
9) hair salon
10) airport
11) zoo

1) gakkoo

_____

2) kyookai

_____

3) eegakan

_____

4) yuubinkyoku

_____

5) ginkoo

_____

6) kooen

_____

7) byooin

_____

8) bijutsukan

_____

9) biyooin

_____

10) kuukoo

_____

11) doobutsuen

_____

3 Hobbies

1) ryoori
(cooking)

_____

2) ryokoo
(trip)

_____

3) undoo
(exercise)

_____

よむれんしゅう｜Reading practice

▶See *TOBIRA I* L1 #3 (p.51).

In order to get to know the Japan House (JH) members better, read their member profiles on the JH Bulletin Board.

Understanding Japanese sentence structure: X は Y です

1）In the profiles below, circle the particles は and の and underline です as in the example.

りょこう：trip　ニューデリー：New Delhi　かんじ：kanji
Nyuuderii

Ex. はじめまして。わたし（は）マーク・シルバです。
Maaku　Shiruba
ゴーブルだいがく（の）よねんせいです。せんこうは　せいじです。
Gooburu
しゅみは　りょこうです。どうぞ　よろしく。

はじめまして。ぼくは　リーマン・ゴルドです。ゴーブルだいが
Riiman　Gorudo　Gooburu
くの　いちねんせいです。じゅうななさいです。しゅっしんは
インドの　ニューデリーです。せんこうは　すうがくです。すうが
Indo　Nyuuderii
くと　かんじが　すきです。よろしく　おねがいします。

はじめまして。わたしは　タオ・ホワン
Tao　Howan
です。はたちです。しゅっしんは
マレーシアです。にねんせいです。せん
Mareeshia
こうは　こうがくです。しゅ
みは　おんがくです。よろ
しく　おねがいします。

はじめまして。アイ・ブルーノです。
Ai　Buruuno
いま、だいがくの　にねんせいです。
せんこうは　びじゅつと　にほんご
です。ネコが　だいすき
neko
です。どうぞ　よろしく
おねがいします。
ネコ
neko

Sorting information

2）Fill in the table below with the information you've learned about the JH members. Insert ✕ if no information is available.

Info / なまえ	マーク・シルバ Maaku　Shiruba	リーマン・ゴルド Riiman　Gorudo	タオ・ホワン Tao　Howan	アイ・ブルーノ Ai　Buruuno
なんねんせい？				
せんこう				
なんさい？				
しゅっしん				
すきなもの／こと (favorite thing)				

かくれんしゅう | Writing practice

▶ Writing sheets are available on the *TOBIRA* website. (See p.6.)

[Self-introduction]

Task: Write your self-introduction in Japanese for your classmates.

① **Pre-writing activity:** Fill in the table with your own information. If you don't know how to spell a proper name in Japanese, provide it in English or the common language in your class.

Info なまえ	
なんねんせい？	
せんこう	
なんさい？	(optional)
しゅっしん	
すきなもの／こと (favorite thing)	

② **Writing:** Using the information above, write your self-introduction in Japanese. Refer to Kim-san's self-introduction on p.46 #9 of *TOBIRA I* and the profiles about the JH members on p.32 of this workbook.

Checklist	
✓	Write horizontally from left to right.
✓	Use all the greetings and sentence structures in the box below.
✓	Use the Japanese period "。" at the end of each sentence. Pay attention to its position. Refer to "Punctuation marks in Japanese" on p.74.
✓	If you don't know how to spell a proper name in Japanese, provide it in English or the common language in your class.

□ はじめまして　　　　□ どうぞよろしくおねがいします
□ XはYです　　　　□ Noun 1 の Noun 2　　　□ （Xは）Yが {すきです／だいすきです}

Exit Check ☑

Now go back to the Hiragana List (p.10) and check if you can read and write all hiragana correctly.

Lesson 2

しゅうまつになにをしますか。
What are you doing over the weekend?

Katakana List できる**Check** ☑

After learning all katakana, come back to this chart to see if you can read and write all characters.

ン	ワ	ラ	ヤ	マ	ハ	ナ	タ	サ	カ	ア
		リ		ミ	ヒ	ニ	チ	シ	キ	イ
		ル	ユ	ム	フ	ヌ	ツ	ス	ク	ウ
		レ		メ	ヘ	ネ	テ	セ	ケ	エ
	(ヲ)*	ロ	ヨ	モ	ホ	ノ	ト	ソ	コ	オ

* ヲ is rarely used in modern Japanese.

At a camp site Which katakana words can you recognize?

カタカナのれんしゅう | Katakana practice

① Trace the gray katakana first, then write each katakana as neatly as you can in the boxes below.

Lesson 2

| S=stop F=flick R=release C=curved line ↓→=direction |

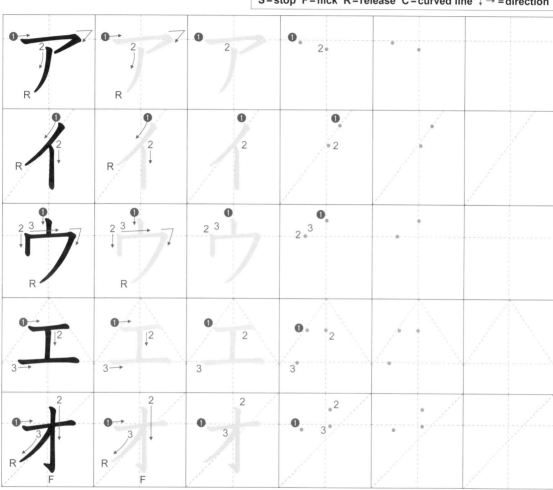

② Write the stroke order of the stroke in red as in the example.

Ex. _____2nd_____   1) _____

2) _____   3) _____

③ Circle the mistake(s) in each katakana, then write the correct one in the box below.

Ex.   1)   2)   3)   4)

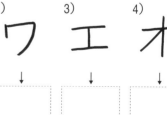

Trace the gray katakana first, then write each katakana as neatly as you can in the boxes below.

S=stop　F=flick　R=release　C=curved line　↓→=direction

カ　キ　ク　ケ　コ

ガ　ギ　グ　ゲ　ゴ

Insert a diacritical mark ＼ for each katakana in the appropriate place at the correct angle.

カ　キ　ク　ケ　コ

⑤ Choose the correct stroke order for each katakana.

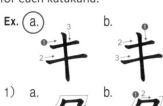

Ex. (a.)   b.

1) a.   b.

2) a.   b.

⑥ Circle the mistake(s) in each katakana, then write the correct one in the box below.

Ex.   1)   2) KU   3) KE   4)

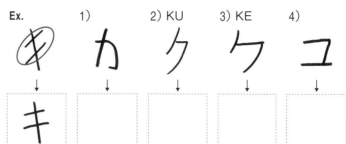

⑦ Match the following katakana to their hiragana equivalents.

1)

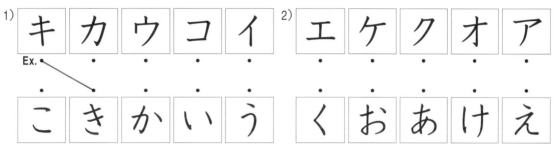

キ　カ　ウ　コ　イ   2) エ　ケ　ク　オ　ア

Ex.

こ　き　か　い　う　　く　お　あ　け　え

⑧ Choose the first katakana for each of the words represented by the pictures below.

Ex. ___a.___   1) _____   2) _____   3) _____   4) _____   5) _____

 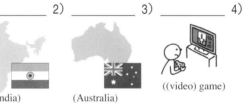

(USA)　　　(India)　　　(Australia)　　((video) game)　　(anime)　　(computer)

a. ア   b. ア   c. オ   d. ゲ   e. イ   f. コ

⑨ Trace the gray katakana first, then rewrite each word in the space provided. Write horizontally or vertically, following the arrow.

1)    2)   3)   4)   5)

(oyster)   (chrysanthemum)   (care)   (Ai)

エ コ　　カ キ　　キ ク　　ケ ア　　ア イ

6)

(cacao)

カ	
カ	
オ	

7)

(kiwi (fruit))

キ	
ウ	
イ	

8)

(Gaia)

ガ	
イ	
ア	

9)

(wear)

ウ	
エ	
ア	

10)

(silkworm)

カ	
イ	
コ	

⑩ Convert each hiragana word into katakana in the space provided, following the arrow.

1) か き

(persimmon)

2) あ い あ い

(aye-aye)

3) こ け

(moss)

4) こ こ あ

COCOA

5) う き き

screech!

6) ご く ご く

gulp, gulp

7) ぎが

SD CARD 16GB

_____

(giga)

8) ぎあ

_____

(gear)

9) こあ

core

_____

(core)

10) いか

_____

(squid)

11) おけ

_____

(short for "orchestra")

12) えご

EGO

_____

カタカナのれんしゅう │ Katakana practice

① Trace the gray katakana first, then write each katakana as neatly as you can in the boxes below.

S=stop F=flick R=release C=curved line ↓ → =direction

サ	ザ	サ			
シ diagonal line	シ diagonal line	シ			
ス	ス	ス			
セ	セ	セ			
ソ steep diagonal line	ゾ steep diagonal line	ソ			
ザ	ザ		ゼ	ゼ	
ジ	ジ		ゾ	ゾ	
ズ	ズ				

Insert a diacritical mark 〝 for each katakana in the appropriate place at the correct angle.

サ	シ	ス	セ	ソ

S=stop F=flick R=release C=curved line ↓ → =direction

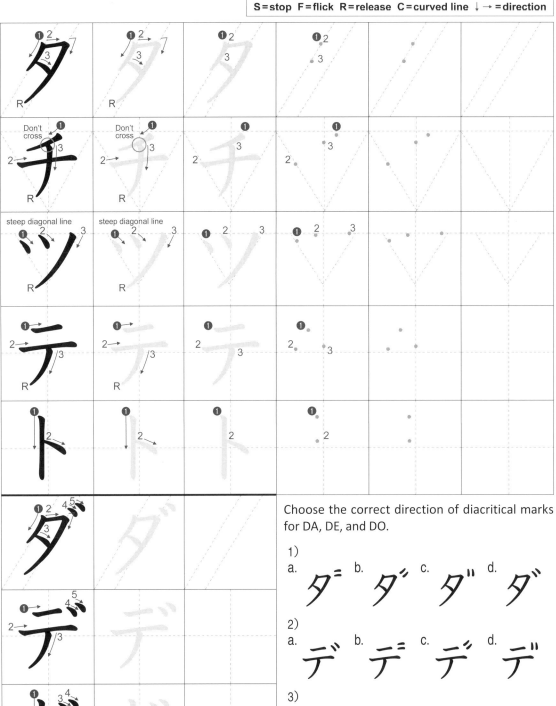

Choose the correct direction of diacritical marks for DA, DE, and DO.

1)
a. ダ゠   b. ダ゛   c. ダ゛   d. ダ

2)
a. デ   b. テ゠   c. テ゛   d. テ゛

3)
a. ド゠   b. ド   c. ド゠   d. ド

Class: _____ Name: _____

★2 Choose the correct starting point (= the red dot) for each stroke shown in black.

Ex. せ
a. b.
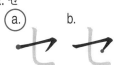

1) し
a. b.

2) つ
a. b.

3) そ
a. b.

Lesson **2**

★3 Choose the katakana equivalent of the following hiragana.

Ex. た
a. b.

1) て
a. b.

2) そ
a. b.
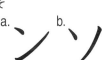

3) し
a. b.

★4 Read the following katakana words aloud and match them to the pictures below.

Ex. アジア (d.)　　1) タスク (　　)　　2) シカゴ (　　)　　3) アウトドア(　　)

a.

(outdoor)

b.

c.

d.

★5 Trace the gray katakana first, then rewrite each word in the space provided. Write horizontally or vertically, following the arrow.

1)

サ	イ	ト

2)

(test)

テ	ス	ト

3)

(idea)

ア	イ	デ	ア

4)

(Germany)

ド	イ	ツ

5)

(do so ti)

ド	ソ	シ

6)

(walrus)

セ	イ	ウ	チ

41

7)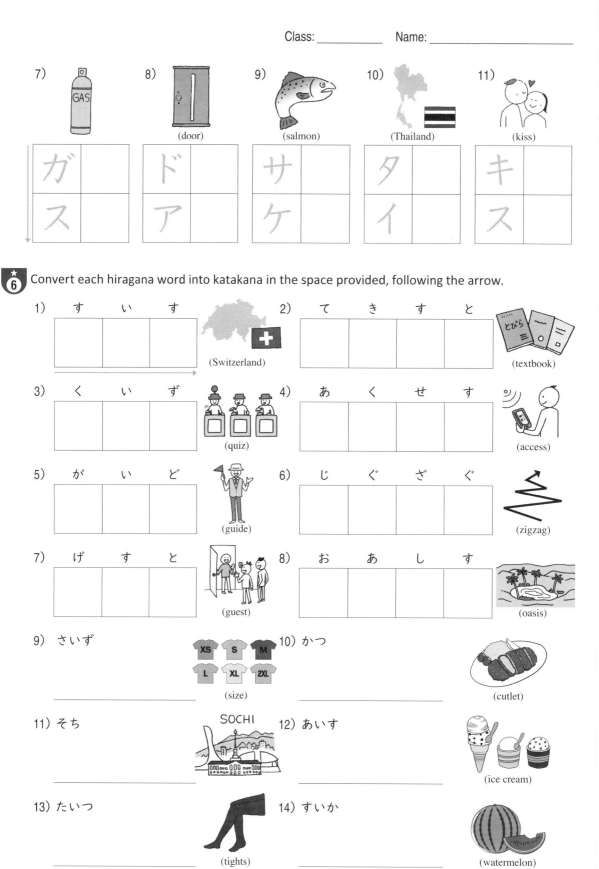

ガ
ス

8) (door)

ド
ア

9) (salmon)

サ
ケ

10) (Thailand)

タ
イ

11) (kiss)

キ
ス

6 Convert each hiragana word into katakana in the space provided, following the arrow.

1) す　い　す

(Switzerland)

2) て　き　す　と

(textbook)

3) く　い　ず

(quiz)

4) あ　く　せ　す

(access)

5) が　い　ど

(guide)

6) じ　ぐ　ざ　ぐ

(zigzag)

7) げ　す　と

(guest)

8) お　あ　し　す

(oasis)

9) さいず

(size)

10) かつ

(cutlet)

11) そち

(SOCHI)

12) あいす

(ice cream)

13) たいつ

(tights)

14) すいか

(watermelon)

カタカナのれんしゅう | Katakana practice

⭐1 Trace the gray katakana first, then write each katakana as neatly as you can in the boxes below.

S = stop F = flick R = release C = curved line ↓ → = direction

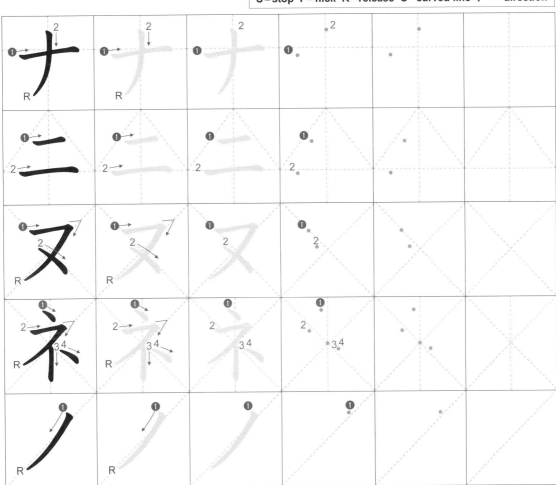

⭐2 Read the following katakana words aloud and match them to the pictures below.

1) テニス （　　） 2) カナダ （　　） 3) サウナ （　　） 4) アイヌ （　　）

5) ツナ （　　） 6) ケニア （　　） 7) カジノ （　　） 8) ネクタイ （　　）

a.

(Canada)

b.

(The Ainu)

c.

(tennis)

d.

(TUNA)

e.

(CASINO)

f.

(necktie)

g.

(sauna)

h.
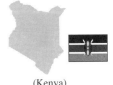
(Kenya)

43

3 Trace the gray katakana first, then write each katakana as neatly as you can in the boxes below.

| S=stop F=flick R=release C=curved line ↓ → =direction |

ハ ヒ フ ヘ ホ バ ベ ビ ボ ブ

Insert a diacritical mark ゛ for each katakana in the appropriate place at the correct angle.

ハ ヒ フ ヘ ホ

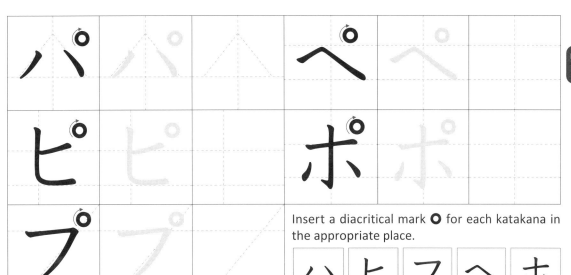

Lesson 2

Insert a diacritical mark **O** for each katakana in the appropriate place.

ハ ヒ フ ヘ ホ

④ Write the stroke order of the stroke in red.

1) _____ 2) _____ 3) _____ 4) _____ 5) _____ 6) _____

ニ ナ ヌ ネ ヒ ホ

⑤ Circle the mistake(s) in each katakana, then write the correct one in the box below.

1) 2) 3) 4) 5)

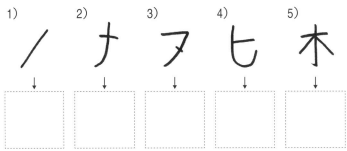

⑥ Trace the gray katakana first, then rewrite each word in the space provided. Write horizontally or vertically, following the arrow.

1)
(pizza)

2) $nano = 10^{-9}$

3)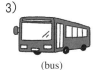
(bus)

4)
(dog)

5)
(cat)

ピ	ザ

ナ	ノ

バ	ス

イ	ヌ

ネ	コ

6)
(crab)

カ	
ニ	

7)
(boss)

ボ	
ス	

8)
(pig)

ブ	
タ	

9)
(operation)

オ	
ペ	

10)
(eggplant)

ナ	
ス	

---

⑦ Convert each hiragana word into katakana in the space provided, following the arrow.

1)　ぽ　す　と

→

(mailbox)

2)　は　い　ち

(Haiti)

3)　ぴ　あ　の

(piano)

4)　に　き　び

(acne)

5)　き　つ　ね

(fox)

6)　た　ぬ　き

(racoon dog)

7)　ひつじ

_____
(sheep)

8)　へび

_____
(snake)

9)　ないふ

_____
(knife)

10)　ばいく

_____
(motorcycle)

11)　たばこ

_____
(cigerette)

12)　ばなな

_____
(banana)

13)　えじぷと

_____
(Egypt)

14)　ぱす

_____
(pass)

Class: ____________ Name: ____________________________

カタカナのれんしゅう | Katakana practice

1 Trace the gray katakana first, then write each katakana as neatly as you can in the boxes below.

S=stop F=flick R=release C=curved line ↓ → =direction

❶→ マ 2 S	❶→ マ 2 S	❶ マ 2	❶ 2		
❶ 2 3 ミ	❶ 2 3 ミ	❶ 2 3 ミ	❶ 2 3		
❶ 2 ム S	❶ 2 ム S	❶ 2 ム	❶ 2		
❶ 2 メ R	❶ 2 メ R	❶ 2 メ	❶ 2		
Don't cross ❶→ 2→ 3 モ C S	Don't cross ❶→ 2→ 3 モ C S	❶ 2 3 モ	❶ 2 3		
❶→ 2 ヤ sharp turn	❶→ 2 ヤ sharp turn	❶ 2 ヤ	❶ 2		
❶→ 2→ ユ	❶→ 2→ ユ	❶ 2 ユ	❶ 2		
❶→ 2→ 3→ ヨ	❶→ 2→ 3→ ヨ	❶ 2 3 ヨ	❶ 2 3		

Class: _____   Name: _____

 2 Write the stroke order of the stroke in red.

1) _____ 2) _____ 3) _____ 4) _____ 5) _____ 6) _____

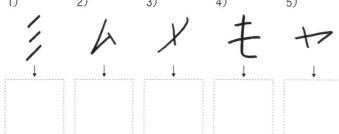

ミ ム メ モ ヤ ヨ

3 Circle the mistake(s) in each katakana, then write the correct one in the box below.

1)　　　　　2)　　　　　3)　　　　　4)　　　　　5)

ミ　ム　メ　モ　ヤ

↓　　　↓　　　↓　　　↓　　　↓

[ ]　[ ]　[ ]　[ ]　[ ]

4 Read the following katakana words aloud and match them to the pictures below.

1) モナコ (　) 2) ガム (　) 3) マイナス (　) 4) ポテト (　) 5) ハム (　)

6) ダム 　(　) 7) メモ (　) 8) シグマ 　(　) 9) ドバイ (　) 10) ジム (　)

a.

(ham)

b.

(dam)

c.

(minus)

d.

(sigma)

e.

MONACO

f.

(gym)

g.

MEMO

h.

(French fries)

i.

((chewing) gum)

j.

DUBAI

5 Trace the gray katakana first, then rewrite each word in the space provided. Write horizontally or vertically, following the arrow.

1) Anime

2)

(Ayutthaya)

3)

(Vietnam)

アニメ　アユタヤ　ベトナム

48

4)

(Claude Monet)

モ	
ネ	

5)

(yoga)

ヨ	
ガ	

6)

(palm)

ヤ	
シ	

7)

(trash)

ゴ	
ミ	

8)

(Mayan)

マ	
ヤ	

Lesson 2

6 Convert each hiragana word into katakana in the space provided, following the arrow.

1)   す　ま　ほ

(smartphone)

2)   ま　い　く

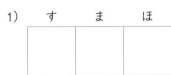
(microphone)

3)   み　す　と

(mist)

4)   ば　は　ま

(The Bahamas)

5)   ぐ　あ　む

GUAM
(Guam)

6)   ま　す　く

(face mask)

7)　めきしこ

_____
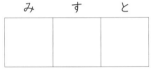
(Mexico)

8)　めそぽたみあ

_____

(Mesopotamia)

9)　ゆず

_____

(Yuzu
(Japanese citrus))

10)　まうす

_____

((computer) mouse)

11)　よせみて

_____

YOSEMITE

12)　でも

_____

(short for "demonstration")

13)　ねずみ

_____

(mouse)

14)　やぎ

_____

(goat)

カタカナのれんしゅう | Katakana practice

★1 Trace the gray katakana first, then write each katakana as neatly as you can in the boxes below.

S=stop F=flick R=release C=curved line ↓ → =direction

ラ	ラ	ラ	ラ		
リ	リ	リ	リ		
ル	ル	ル	ル		
レ	レ	レ	レ		
ロ	ロ	ロ	ロ		
ワ	ワ	ワ	ワ		
ヲ	ヲ	ヲ	ヲ		
ン	ン	ン	ン		

② Choose the correct stroke order for each katakana.

1) a.   b.

2) a.   b.

3) a.   b.

③ Circle the mistake(s) in each katakana, then write the correct one in the box below.

1)   2)   3)   4)   5)

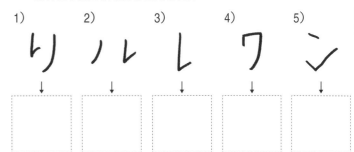

④ Circle the katakana equivalents to the following hiragana.

Ex. う [ウ・ワ]   1) く [ク・ケ]   2) こ [ユ・コ]   3) す [ヌ・ス]   4) せ [セ・ヒ]

5) そ [ソ・ン]   6) た [ク・タ]   7) つ [シ・ツ]   8) て [チ・テ]   9) の [メ・ノ]

10) ま [ア・マ]   11) め [メ・ナ]   12) ら [フ・ラ]   13) る [ル・レ]   14) わ [ワ・ク]

⑤ Read the following katakana words aloud and match them to the pictures below.

1) テレビ (   )   2) ドル   (   )   3) バイオリン (   )

4) トイレ (   )   5) サラダ (   )

a.

(toilet)

b.

(TV)

c.

(dollar)

d.

(salad)

e.

(violin)

⑥ Match the following country names in katakana to their English equivalents in the box below.

Ex. インド (e.)   1) インドネシア (   )   2) ブラジル (   )   3) フランス   (   )

4) ロシア (   )   5) モンゴル   (   )   6) スペイン (   )   7) アイルランド(   )

8) チリ   (   )   9) コロンビア   (   )   10) アメリカ (   )   11) イタリア (   )

| a. Brazil | b. Chile | c. Columbia | d. France | e. India | f. Indonesia |
| g. Ireland | h. Italy | i. Mongolia | j. Spain | k. Russia | l. USA |

★7 Trace the gray katakana first, then rewrite each word in the space provided, following the arrow.

1) (class)

クラス

2) (living room)

リビング

3) (hotel)

ホテル

4) (wine)

ワイン

5) (present)

プレゼント

6) (zero)

ゼロ

★8 Convert each hiragana word into katakana in the space provided, following the arrow.

1) あ ぷ り

(app)

2) こ ん び に

(convenience store)

3) だ ん す

(dance)

4) い べ ん と

(event)

5) ぷろぐらむ

_____

(program)

6) くりすます

_____

(Christmas)

7) れすとらん

_____

(restaurant)

8) あるばいと

_____

(part-time job)

9) ぱそこん

_____

(computer)

10) わんわん

woof-woof!

れんしゅう | Practice

 Read the katakana words aloud and match them to their English equivalents.

1) Double consonants: small ツ

Ex. バッグ •　　　　　• ticket

a. キッチン •　　　　　• bag

b. ネット •　　　　　　• kitchen

c. チケット •　　　　　• (inter)net

2) Contracted sounds: small ヤユヨ

a. キャンプ •　　　　　• chocolate

b. ニュアンス •　　　　• nuance

c. チョコ •　　　　　　• jogging

d. ジョギング •　　　　• camp

3) Long vowels: [er], [ar], [ei], [or], [ou], etc.

a. アパート •　　　　　• flute

b. ビーチ •　　　　　　• beach

c. フルート •　　　　　• sports

d. マレーシア •　　　　• homestay

e. スポーツ •　　　　　• Malaysia

f. ホームステイ •　　　• apartment

5) Substitution of sounds that don't exist in Japanese: [th], [l] and [r]

a. スミス •　　　　　　• healthy

b. ブラザー •　　　　　• Thank you.

c. バースデー •　　　　• brother

d. サンキュー •　　　　• birthday

e. ヘルシー •　　　　　• Smith

f. マラソン •　　　　　• marathon

4) Special sounds and small アイウエオ
(Refer to the chart on p.84 of *TOBIRA I*.)

SH, J, CH, T, and D sounds

a. シェア •　　　　　　• share

b. プロジェクト •　　　• check

c. チェック •　　　　　• project

d. パーティー •　　　　• media

e. メディア •　　　　　• party

F and W sounds

a. ファストフード •　　　• fork

b. オフィス •　　　　　　• office

c. カフェラテ •　　　　　• caffe latte

d. フォーク •　　　　　　• fast food

e. ハロウィン •　　　　　• web

f. ウェブ •　　　　　　　• walking

g. ウォーキング •　　　　• Halloween

V sound

a. ヴァイオリン
　バイオリン 　　　　　• vocal

b. デジャヴ
　デジャブ 　　　　　　• violin

c. ベートーヴェン
　ベートーベン 　　　　• déjà vu

d. ヴォーカル
　ボーカル 　　　　　　• Beethoven

 Match the following city names in katakana to their English equivalents in the box below.

1) ローマ　　　　　(　)　　2) ニューヨーク (　)　　3) プーケット　(　)

4) シンガポール　(　)　　5) パリ　　　　(　)　　6) マチュピチュ (　)

7) ストックホルム (　)　　8) マドリッド　(　)　　9) パース　　　(　)

> a. Machu Picchu　　b. Madrid　　c. New York　　d. Paris　　e. Perth
>
> f. Phuket　　　　　g. Rome　　h. Singapore　　i. Stockholm

3 Trace the gray katakana first, then rewrite each word in the space provided. Write horizontally or vertically, following the arrow. Pay attention to the position and size of the small katakana and the direction of the long vowel symbol (ー).

1) ナッツ

(nut)

2) コンサート

(concert)

3) インターンシップ

(internship)

4) ホストファミリー

(host family)

5) ポップカルチャー

(pop culture)

6) (robot)

ロボット

7) (office)

オフィス

8) (mobile phone)

ケータイ

9) (shower)

シャワー

10) (check)

チェック

4 Write katakana for each word in the picture.

6) けーき
4) ぎたー   5) のーと   7) こーひー
8) げーむ   9) ちょこれーと
3) Tしゃつ
2) べっど
12) せーたー
1) ぺっと
11) じーんず   10) こーら

1) _____   2) _____   3) _____

4) _____   5) _____   6) _____

7) _____   8) _____   9) _____

10) _____   11) _____   12) _____

5 Read the IT-related katakana words aloud and write their English equivalents.

1) メール   (   )   2) インターネット (   )

3) コンピュータ   (   )   4) パスワード   (   )

5) ダウンロード   (   )   6) フォルダー   (   )

6 Fill in the blanks for your self-introduction using katakana. See "Writing names in Japanese" on p.75.

わたしの　なまえは _____です。

しゅっしんは _____の _____です。

7 Type マクドナルド, ピザハット, or スターバックス and メニュー on a search engine. Then, write three menu items in katakana you can recognize.

_____   _____   _____

よむれんしゅう | Reading practice

▶ See *TOBIRA I* L2 #2 (pp.76-77).

Read the passage about Haru's weekly schedule and answer the questions below.

Understanding Japanese sentence structure: Verb sentences

1） Underline the verbs in the passage and mark the accompanying particles used with it: ○ for the time marker, △ for the location/destination marker, and □ for the object marker as in the example. Write your answers in your textbook.

   Ex. ８じはん(に) おきます。 あさ　うち/て\ コーヒー□を のみます。

Compare and contrast

2） First, find out when Haru does the following activities, then **compare** your daily activities with Haru's. **Choose your busiest day of the week** for the comparison.

	a. get up	b. go to first class	c. eat lunch	d. go home	e. go to bed	f. work part-time
When (time or day) Haru does each activity	8:30 AM					
When you do it	____ AM					

Comprehension check

3） Mark ○ if the statement about Haru is true and × if it is false.

   (　　) あさ　うちで　コーヒーを　のみます。

   (　　) まいにち　だいがくに　いきます。

   (　　) かようびと　もくようびに　クラブで　えいごを　はなします。

   (　　) ルームメートと　よく　レストランで　ばんごはんを　たべます。

   (　　) あまり　クラスの　べんきょうを　しません。

   (　　) ときどき　SNSと　テレビを　みます。

4） Answer the questions about yourself.

   a. まいにち　あさごはんを　たべますか。　　_____

   b. なんようびに　だいがくに　いきますか。　　_____

   c. よく　どこで　しゅくだいを　しますか。　　_____

   d. よく　テレビを　みますか。　　_____

かくれんしゅう | Writing practice

▶ Writing sheets are available on the *TOBIRA* website. (See p.6.)

Lesson
2

〔○○'s daily life〕

Task: Write a short passage about the daily life of yourself or your favorite person, character, etc.

① **Pre-writing activity:** Fill in the table below with the daily schedule of yourself or the person you have chosen to describe. You can fill out the table either in the common language in your class or in Japanese.

Possible activities

_____ の　せいかつ (life)

When?	Where?	What?	When?	Where?	What?
		get up			
Things you/they almost never do or do not do very often					

② **Writing:** Using the ideas you have brainstormed above, describe the daily life of the person you have chosen under the title 「○○の　せいかつ (life)」.

Checklist	
✓	Write horizontally from left to right and use appropriate punctuations.
✓	Link sentences using conjunctions to show how they relate.
✓	Use as many grammar points as possible from the box below.
✓	If you don't know how to spell a proper name in katakana, try writing it in katakana and provide a translation above it.

☐ Verbs (*masu*-form, affirmative)　☐ Verbs (*masu*-form, negative)　☐ Particles: を／に／で
☐ Adverbs of frequency: よく／ときどき／あまり／ぜんぜん
☐ Conjunctions: それから／でも／だから　☐ X は Y が（だい）すきです

Exit Check ☑

Now go back to the Katakana List (p.34) and check if you can read and write all katakana correctly.

Kanji List **できるCheck** ☑

	1	2	3	4	5	6	7	8	9	10	11	12	13	14
Kanji	一	二	三	四	五	六	七	八	九	十	月	私	子	人
Entry Check														
Exit Check														

Events in each month of the year

*Celebration for 3, 5 & 7-year-old children

七五三
the Shichi-go-san celebration*
十一月

おおみそか
New Year's Eve
十二月

おしょうがつ
New Year's Day
一月

せつぶん
the last day of winter
二月

ひなまつり
Doll's Festival
三月

スポーツのひ
Sports Day
十月

おつきみ
moon viewing
九月

なつまつり
summer festival
八月

私
三人かぞく　一人っ子

たなばた
Star Festival
七月

つゆ
rainy season
六月

こどものひ
Children's Day
五月

にゅうがくしき
entrance ceremony
四月

Kanji in daily life Which kanji can you recognize?

かんじのれんしゅう | Kanji practice

① Trace the gray kanji first while following the given stroke order and stoke types (stop, flick, etc.), then write the kanji twice as neatly as possible.

S=stop F=flick R=release C=curved line ↓→=direction ◯=note ⚬=space

Lesson **3**

1	2	3	4	5	6
一	二	三	四	五	六

7	8	9	10	11	12
七	八	九	十	月	私

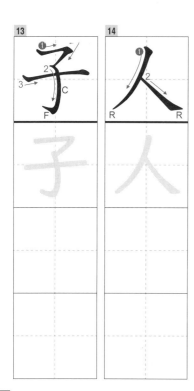

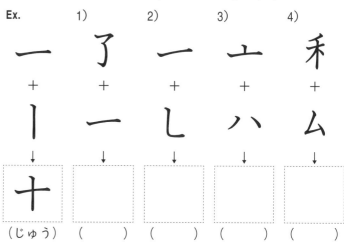

★2 Make a kanji using each element and write it in the box. Then, provide the reading for each kanji in ( ).

Ex.　一 ＋ 丨 ↓ 十（じゅう）

1) 了 ＋ 一 ↓ （　　　）

2) 一 ＋ し ↓ （　　　）

3) 凵 ＋ ハ ↓ （　　　）

4) 禾 ＋ ム ↓ （　　　）

★3 Circle the indicated stroke in each kanji as in the example.

Ex. 月 1st 1) 五 3rd 2) 九 1st 3) 七 1st 4) 十 1st 5) 四 3rd

★4 Circle the mistake(s) in each kanji, then write the correct one in the box.

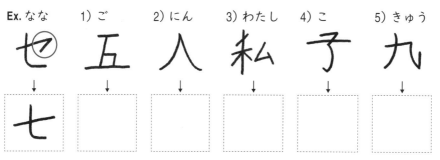

Ex. なな 七 → 七 1) ご 五 → 2) にん 人 → 3) わたし 私 → 4) こ 子 → 5) きゅう 九 →

★5 Provide kanji for the underlined part.

1) わたし<u> </u>

2) フランス<u>じん</u>

3) <u>さんにんきょうだい</u>

4) <u>こども</u>

⑥ The following illustrations indicate the number of players on a team for each type of sport. Write the number in kanji, then provide its reading in ( ).

Ex. バスケットボール

___五人___ （　　ごにん　　）

1) テニス

_____ （　　　　　　　　）

2) ビーチバレー

_____ （　　　　　　　　　）

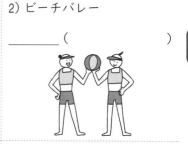

3) やきゅう

_____ （　　　　　　　　）

4) カーリング

_____ （　　　　　　　　）

5) サッカー

_____ （　　　　　　　　）

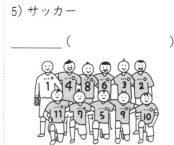

⑦ Write how many people there are in each family.

Ex. ケンさん　　（　三人かぞく　）　　1) ナオミさん　　（　　　　　　　　）

2) マリアさん　（　　　　　　　）　　3) _____ さん　（　　　　　　　）

Ex. ケンさん　　　　　1) ナオミさん　　　　2) マリアさん　　　　3) your own

⑧ Look at Tobira-zushi's grand opening flyer and answer the following questions in hiragana.

Ex. とびらずしのゆうびんばんごう (postal code) は　なんばんですか。

　　　いちにさんの　よんごろくななです。

1) とびらずしのでんわばんごうは　なんばんですか。

_____

2) とびらずしのファックス (FAX) ばんごうは　なんばんですか。

_____

3) とびらずしは　なん月（がつ）　オープンですか。

_____

四月オープン

〒123-4567

E-mail tobira-zushi@tobira.jp
FAX ○一二一三四五一三四五六
TEL ○一二一三四五一六七八九
とびら市とびら町一一三

とびらずし

★★ **9** The chart below is a calendar for fruits in season in Japan. Write the months in which the following fruits are ripe, writing kanji in __ and its reading in ( ).

Ex. メロン   __七月__ (しちがつ) と __八月__ (はちがつ)

1) いちご   _____ (   ) と _____ (   ) と _____ (   )

2) ブルーベリー   _____ (   ) と _____ (   ) と _____ (   )

3) ようなし   _____ (   ) と _____ (   ) と _____ (   )

4) りんご   _____ (   ) と _____ (   ) と _____ (   )

★★ **10** Read the following information about Yamada-san, and choose the appropriate reading from a.-c. for the underlined kanji.

Ex. 四人きょうだいです。   [a. し   (b.)よ   c. よん]

1) やまださんは　四ねんせいです。   [a. し   b. よ   c. よん]

2) 二十四さいです。   [a. にじゅうし   b. にじゅうよ   c. にじゅうよん]

3) たんじょうび (birthday) は　四月です。 [a. し   b. よ   c. よん]

4) いもうとは　二十一さいです。   [a. にじゅうい   b. にじゅういち c. にじゅういっ]

5) おとうとは　十八さいです。   [a. じゅうは   b. じゅうはち   c. じゅうはっ]

6) やまださんは　九人かぞくです。   [a. きゅう   b. くう   c. きゅ]

7) よく　九じごろ　ジムに　いきます。 [a. きゅう   b. く   c. きゅ]

★★ **11** Choose a kanji from the list below to fill in the box in the middle to make four words. Each word should be read in the direction that the arrow indicates. Then, provide the reading for each word.

┌──────────────────────────────────┐
│ **Kanji List:** 八　私　四　人　子 │
└──────────────────────────────────┘

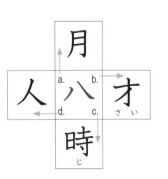

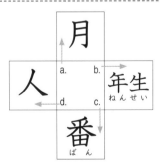

Ex. Kanji in the center: __八__

a. __はちがつ__   b. __はっさい__

c. __はちじ__   d. __はちにん__

1) Kanji in the center: _____

a. _____   b. _____

c. _____   d. _____

2) Kanji in the center: _____

a. _____   b. _____

c. _____   d. _____

12 Provide the kanji for the underlined hiragana words in the following sentences. The numbers in ( ) indicate the total number of kanji that should be provided.

1) <u>わたし</u>は　<u>ごにん</u>かぞくです。きょうだいは　<u>ふたり</u>です。(4)
　　Ex. 私　　　a.　　　　　　　　　　　　　　　　　　b.

2) だいがくの<u>いち</u>ねんせいです。いま、<u>じゅうきゅう</u>さいです。(3)
　　　　　　　a.　　　　　　　　　　b.

3) <u>こども</u>のとき、よく　<u>ろくがつ</u>と　<u>しちがつ</u>に　りょこうしました。(5)
　a.　　　　　　　　　　b.　　　　　　c.

4) スミスさんは　アメリカ<u>じん</u>です。<u>ひとりっこ</u>です。(4)
　　　　　　　　　　　　　a.　　　　　b.

5) スミスさんは　<u>じゅうはっ</u>さいです。たんじょうび (birthday) は　<u>しがつ</u>です。(4)
　　　　　　　　a.　　　　　　　　　　　　　　　　　　　　　b.

13 Make a presentation about a family from your favorite anime/manga/dramas/movies/books, or your own/dream family.

★★ **Step 1** Provide the reading for the kanji of the underlined words.

　　<u>私</u>は　アニメの『たなかさんのかぞく』が　すきです。
　　Ex. わたし

たなかさんは　<u>三人</u>かぞくです。たなかさんと　おとうさんと
　　　　　　　a.

おかあさんです。それから、ペットのたろうです。たなかさんは

<u>一人っ子</u>です。たなかさんは　<u>二十一</u>さいです。たんじょうびは
b.　　　　　　　　　　　　　c.

<u>四月</u>です。だいがくの<u>三</u>ねんせいです。おとうさんは　<u>五十</u>さいです。おかあさんは
d.　　　　　　　e.　　　　　　　　　　　　　　　f.

<u>四十八</u>さいです。たろうは　<u>七</u>さいです。
g.　　　　　　　　　　h.

　　たなかさんは　まいにち　<u>六</u>じごろ　おきます。それから、<u>七</u>じごろ　あさごはんを　たべ
　　　　　　　　　　　i.　　　　　　　　　　　　　　j.

ます。<u>八</u>じごろに　だいがくに　いきます。<u>四</u>じごろ　いえに　かえります。<u>五</u>じごろに
　　k.　　　　　　　　　　　　　　　l.　　　　　　　　　　　　　　m.

たろうと　こうえんに　いきます。<u>九</u>じごろ　ねます。たなかさんのかぞくは　<u>七月</u>に　よく
　　　　　　　　　　　　　n.　　　　　　　　　　　　　　　　　　o.

りょこうします。

★★★ **Step 2** Write a presentation script about the family you have chosen. Use kanji that you have learned in L3 as much as possible.

| **Information to include** | family name & structure | each family member's name & age |
| | their daily schedule | family activities |

よむれんしゅう | Reading practice

▶ See *TOBIRA I* L3 #2 (pp.107-108).

Read Ai's composition about her summer break and answer the questions below.

Identifying the subject and verb of a sentence

1） Find each sentence with a past tense verb in Ai's composition and underline the verb. Then, choose who did each action from the box below. Write your answers in your textbook.

　●**Check Point:** In Japanese, it is common to omit information that could be understood from the context without being explicitly stated.

Ai (**A**)	tour guide (**G**)	tour participants (**P**)	Ai's family (**F**)	readers (**R**)

　Exs. きょうとに　<u>いきました</u>。（A）　　おみやげのみせを　<u>みました</u>。（A）

Recognizing sequence

2） Put the following activities a.-f. that Ai did on her trip in the correct order.

　　　(　a 　) → (　　　) → (　　　) → (　　　) → (　　　) → (　　　)

a. went on a market tour	b. went to a *wagashi* shop	c. ate various Japanese snacks
d. made *wagashi*	e. took photos	f. met her family

Comprehension check

3） Mark ○ if the statement is true and × if it is false.

　（　　　）　アイさんは　がっこうのともだちと　きょうとに　いきました。

　（　　　）　ツアーのガイドの人は　にほんごを　はなしました。だから、アイさんは　えいごを
　　　　　　　はなしませんでした。

　（　　　）　アイさんは　いちばで　しゃしんを　とりました。

　（　　　）　アイさんは　いちばで　にほんのたべものを　たくさん　かいました。

　（　　　）　アイさんは　わがしを　つくりましたが、かぞくは　つくりませんでした。

4） Respond to Ai's last sentence in the passage:「私と　いっしょに　わがしを　つくりませんか。」

_____

かくれんしゅう | Writing practice

▶ Writing sheets are available on the *TOBIRA* website. (See p.6.)

Sharing a travel experience

Task: Write a blog post in Japanese about a memorable trip you have gone on.

1 **Pre-writing activity:** Organize the information about your experience. You can write the information either in Japanese or in the common language in your class.

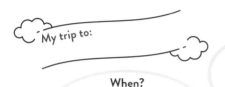

My trip to:

When?

Where did you go?

Who did you go with?

What was special about this trip?

What did you do?

How did you feel?

☐ よかったです
(It was good.)

☐ おもしろかったです
(It was interesting.)

☐ きれいでした
(It was beautiful/clean.)

2 **Writing:** Using the ideas you have brainstormed above, write about your trip under the title
「_____ のりょこう」.
(the place)

Checklist	
✓	Write horizontally from left to right and use appropriate punctuations.
✓	Link sentences using conjunctions to show how they relate.
✓	Use as many grammar points as possible from the box below.
✓	Use as many learned kanji as possible.
✓	If you don't know how to spell a proper name in katakana, try writing it in katakana and provide a translation above it.

☐ Verbs (*masu*-form, **past**-affirmative)   ☐ Verbs (*masu*-form, **past**-negative)

☐ と [Accompaniment marker]   ☐ は [Contrast marker]

☐ や [Noun-listing particle]   ☐ が [Contrast conjunction]

☐ Conjunctions: それから／でも／だから   ☐ ～ませんか／～ましょう

Exit Check ☑

Now go back to the Kanji List for this lesson (p.58) and do the exit check to see what kanji you can read and write.

Kanji List できるCheck ✓

	15	16	17	18	19	20	21	22	23	24	25	26	27	28	29	30	31
Kanji	百	千	万	円	曜	日	火	水	木	金	土	学	生	先	年	大	小
Entry Check																	
Exit Check																	

Days of the week　Name origins and space trivia

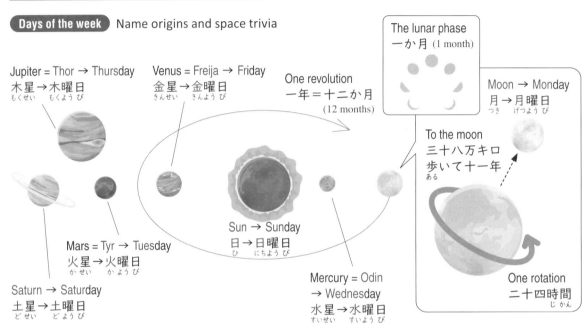

Jupiter = Thor → Thursday
木星→木曜日
もくせい　もくようび

Venus = Freija → Friday
金星→金曜日
きんせい　きんようび

One revolution
一年＝十二か月
(12 months)

The lunar phase
一か月 (1 month)

Moon → Monday
月→月曜日
つき　げつようび

To the moon
三十八万キロ
歩いて十一年
ある

Sun → Sunday
日→日曜日
ひ　にちようび

Mars = Tyr → Tuesday
火星→火曜日
かせい　かようび

Mercury = Odin
→ Wednesday
水星→水曜日
すいせい　すいようび

Saturn → Saturday
土星→土曜日
どせい　どようび

One rotation
二十四時間
じかん

Kanji in daily life　Which kanji can you recognize?

学生割引
✦10%OFF!✦
大学生
&
専門学校生

小さいサイズ ～ 大きいサイズ

XXS ▶▶▶ 5L

あなたのサイズがみつかる！

10000　壱万円
5000　五千円
1000　千円　1000

平日限定 日替わりメニュー
全品750円

月曜日　豚しょうが焼き丼
火曜日　大海老天丼
木曜日　ロースカツ丼
水曜日　とりそぼろ丼
金曜日　ローストビーフ丼
うどん or そばセット +250円

かんじのれんしゅう｜Kanji practice

1 Trace the gray kanji first while following the given stroke order and stoke types (stop, flick, etc.), then write the kanji twice as neatly as possible.

S = stop F = flick R = release C = curved line ↓ → = direction ◯ = note ◌ = space

15	16	17	18	19	20
百	千	万	円	曜	日

Lesson **4**

17: Don't cross

21	22	23	24	25	26
火	水	木	金	土	学

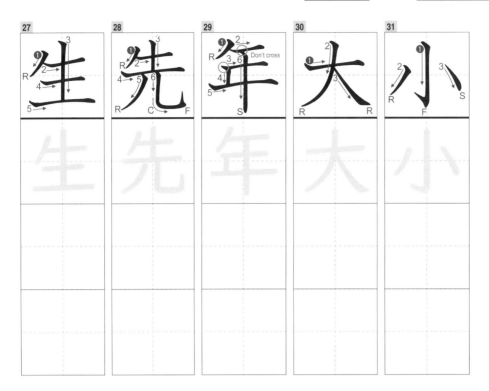

2 Circle the indicated stroke in each kanji as in the example.

Ex.	1)	2)	3)	4)	5)

Ex. 水 (1st) 1) 日 (3rd) 2) 万 (2nd) 3) 木 (2nd) 4) 火 (3rd) 5) 金 (5th)

3 Make a kanji using each element and write it in the box. Then, provide the reading for each kanji in ( ).

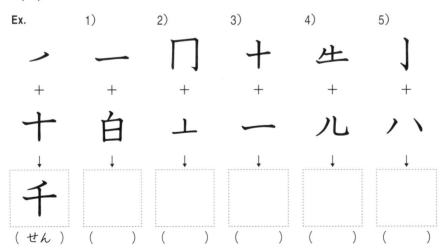

Ex. ノ + 十 → 千 (せん)   1) 一 + 白 → (   )   2) 冂 + 工 → (   )   3) 十 + 一 → (   )   4) 生 + 儿 → (   )   5) 亅 + 八 → (   )

④ Circle the mistake(s) in each kanji, then write the correct one in the box.

| Ex. ひゃく | 1) まん | 2) ねん | 3) せい | 4) きん | 5) か | 6) がく |

  年 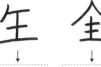 火
↓ ↓ ↓ ↓ ↓ ↓ ↓

百

⑤ First, read かんじのはなし on p.127 of *TOBIRA I*. Then, provide the reading for the underlined kanji and mark whether it is an *on-* or a *kun-yomi*.

おんよみ？ くんよみ？

	Reading	おん	くん		Reading	おん	くん
Ex.1 十月	じゅう	◯		Ex.2 十ください	とお		◯
1) 大きい				2) 大学			
3) 水をのみます				4) 水曜日			
5) 一年生				6) 一つ			
7) 五人				8) 五つ			
9) 八じ				10) 八つ			
11) 金曜日				12) お金			
13) 日本				14) 日曜日			

⑥ Based on the pictures provided, fill in each __ with the appropriate word using kanji from the boxes below. Add *okurigana** as necessary. Then, provide its reading in (   ). You may use the same kanji more than once.

* *Okurigana* is the conjugating part written in hiragana for adjectives and verbs and is necessary to complete these words.

Choices for 1) & 2): 火　生　学　日　曜　先　月

1) 佐藤さんは___Ex.先生___です。スミスさんは_____です。
　　（　せんせい　）　　　　　　（　　　　　　　）

2) 佐藤さんのオフィスアワーは_____と_____です。
　　　　　　　（　　　　　）（　　　　　　）

Prof. Sato's **OFFICE HOURS**
Mon. 8am to 5pm
Tue. 8am to 5pm

Choices for 3) & 4): 年　人　大　小　日　先

3) スミスさんは_____イヌが好きです。
　　　　　（　　　　　）

4) 佐藤さんは_____イヌが好きです。
　　　　　（　　　　　）

69

7 Choose the correct combination of kanji and its *okurigana*.

Ex. サンドイッチを［a. 二っっ　b. 二たつ　ⓒ二つ］ください。

1) パンを［a. 三つつ　b. 三っつ　c. 三つ］ください。

2) ケーキを［a. 五っつ　b. 五つ　c. 五つつ］ください。

3) コーヒーを［a. 一つ　b. 一とつ　c. 一っつ］ください。

4)［a. 大い　b. 大きい　c. 大おきい］ケーキですね。

5) 私の町は［a. 小いさい　b. 小い　c. 小さい］町です。
まち　　　　　　　　　　　　　　　　　　　　　　　　　　　まち

Ah! I see a pattern for the combinations of kanji and general counter 〜つ！

8 Suppose you are at a popular bakery in Japan now. Provide the number for each type of items 1)-9) that the bakery has in kanji as well as its reading in hiragana.

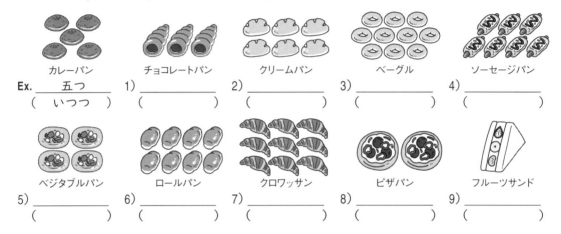

カレーパン　　　チョコレートパン　　クリームパン　　　ベーグル　　　ソーセージパン

Ex. ____五つ____　1) _____　2) _____　3) _____　4) _____
（　いつつ　）　（　　　　　）　（　　　　　）　（　　　　　）　（　　　　　）

ベジタブルパン　　　ロールパン　　　クロワッサン　　　ピザパン　　　フルーツサンド

5) _____　6) _____　7) _____　8) _____　9) _____
（　　　　　）　（　　　　　）　（　　　　　）　（　　　　　）　（　　　　　）

Which item and how many of them would you like to buy? _____

(Answer in a complete Japanese sentence.)

9 Below is the lunch special menu of a restaurant called "Tobi~ra."

Step 1 For each lunch, write the day of the week it is served on in ___ and its price in (　) in hiragana.

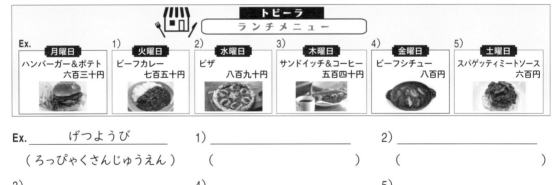

Ex.　月曜日　　　1) 火曜日　　　2) 水曜日　　　3) 木曜日　　　4) 金曜日　　　5) 土曜日
ハンバーガー＆ポテト　ビーフカレー　ピザ　　　サンドイッチ＆コーヒー　ビーフシチュー　スパゲッティミートソース
六百三十円　　　七百五十円　　八百九十円　　五百四十円　　八百円　　　六百円

Ex.____げつようび____　1) _____　2) _____
（ろっぴゃくさんじゅうえん）　（　　　　　　　　　　）　（　　　　　　　　　　）

3) _____　4) _____　5) _____
（　　　　　　　　　　）　（　　　　　　　　　　）　（　　　　　　　　　　）

Step 2 Answer the following questions about your choice in Japanese. Use complete sentences.

何を食べますか。 _____　　何曜日に行きますか。 _____
なに　た　　　　　　　　　　　　　　　　　　　　　なんよう び　い

いくらですか。 _____

★★ 10 Provide the kanji for the underlined hiragana words in the following sentences. Add *okurigana** as necessary. The numbers in ( ) indicate the total number of kanji that should be provided.

* See p.69 #6.

Ex. わたしの家はおおきいです。（2）
　　私　　　　大きい

1）私の兄はだいがくせいです。今、よねんせいです。
　　　あに　　a.　　　　いま　　b.

　　妹 はじゅうろくさいです。（8）
　　いもうと　　c.

2）せん 週 のにちようびに友達とコンサートに行きました。
　　a.　しゅう　b.　　　　　ともだち　　　　　　い

　　チケットはいちまんにせんえんでした。（9）
　　　　　　c.

3）どようびにネコカフェに行きました。ひとりで行きました。
　　a.　　　　　　　　い　　　　　　b.　　い

　　ネコカフェでちいさいネコを見ました。それから、コーヒーとみずを飲みました。
　　　　　　　c.　　　み　　　　　　　　　　　　　d.　　の

　　全部で (in total) きゅうひゃくななじゅうえんでした。（12）
　　ぜんぶ　　　　　　e.

Lesson **4**

11 You have just received the following message from Suzuki-san.

★★ [Step 1] Provide the readings for the kanji of the underlined words.

> 私はとびら大学の三年生です。私の大学はとても大きいです。学生は三万人ぐらいです。
> **Ex.** わたし　a.　　b.　　　　　　　　　　c.　　d.　e.
>
> でも、英語のクラスは小さいです。クラスの学生は十五人です。先生はブラウン先生です。
> 　　　えいご　　　　f.　　　　　　　　　g.　　　　h.
>
> クラスは月曜日と水曜日と金曜日です。テキスト (textbook) は二千八百円でした。
> 　　　i.　　j.　　　k.　　　　　　　　　　　l.
>
> 昨日、単語を八つ勉 強 しました。今日は六つ勉 強 します。英語は 難 しいですが、クラスは
> きのう　たんご　m.　べんきょう　　　きょう　n.　べんきょう　えいご　むずか
>
> 楽しいです。先月はクラスメートといっしょにカラオケ (karaoke) に
> たの　　　o.
>
> 行きました。英語の歌を歌いました。とても楽しかったです。
> い　　　えいご　うた　うた　　　　　たの

★★★ [Step 2] Reply to Suzuki-san by writing about your school and Japanese class. Use kanji that you have learned in LL3-4 as much as possible.

Information to include	your affiliation & grade	total number of students
	your teacher's name	class size & schedule
	textbook price	impression of your Japanese class

よむれんしゅう | Reading practice

▶ See *TOBIRA I* L4 #3 (pp.147-148).

Read Mark's restaurant review and answer the questions below.

1）Who ate what? Write the person who ate each item in the table below.

What?	Who?	What?	Who?
すき焼き や		とんかつ	
天ぷらそばセット てん		さくらもち	

Understanding Japanese sentence structure: Adjective sentences

2）There are 10 adjectives (*I*-adj. and *Na*-adj.) conjugated in various ways in Mark's review. Refer to the example on p.147 of *TOBIRA I* and underline the other nine. (If the same adjective appears multiple times, you should count it only once towards the total of nine.)

Identifying the logical connection between sentences

3）Write the most appropriate conjunction from a.-c. into each ☐ in Mark's review to make it more cohesive.

a. でも   b. それから   c. だから

l.3 ☐   l.7 ☐   l.12 ☐

Identifying omitted words

4）**Step 1** Circle each topic marker は in Mark's review and underline the topic of the sentence.

Ex. 昨日(は)土曜日でした。
きのう

Step 2 Refer to p.148 #4 of *TOBIRA I* and insert the missing topics in Mark's review in [　].

Ex. ll.2-3 [　　私　　は]   a. l.7 [　　　　　は]

b. l.9 [　　　　　は]   c. l.15 [　　　　　は]

Comprehension check

5）Mark ○ if the statement is true and × if it is false.

（　　）マークさんは日曜日に日本のレストランに行きました。
　　　　　　　　　　　　　にほん　　　　　　い

（　　）レストランは小さかったです。でも、きれいでした。

（　　）マークさんはこのレストランのすき焼きが好きです。
　　　　　　　　　　　　　　　　　　　　　　や　　す

6）Answer the questions below in Japanese.

a. コンサートホールからレストランまで、どのぐらいかかりましたか。

b. マークさんの家族のご飯は、全部で (in total) いくらでしたか。
　　　　　　かぞく　　はん　ぜんぶ

c. マークさんのお母さんは、さくらもちを何で食べましたか。
　　　　　　　　かあ　　　　　　　　　なに　た

d. 「このレストラン」（ll.15-16）の名前は何ですか。
　　　　　　　　　　　　　　　　　なまえ　なん

かくれんしゅう | Writing practice

▶ Writing sheets are available on the *TOBIRA* website. (See p.6.)

Writing a review: restaurants, activities, etc.

Task: Write a review of a restaurant where you have eaten recently. You may also choose another topic such as アニメ, まんが, コンサート, 映画(えいが), etc.

1 Pre-writing activity: Answer the questions in the table below in simple keywords or phrases. (Do not write full sentences.) You may write them either in Japanese or in the common language in your class.

Lesson 4

What is your topic?	
What did you do?	
How was it? (Your thoughts and impressions)	
Your recommendation/special things you want to mention	
Your comments and/or opinions	
Star rating	☆ ☆ ☆ ☆ ☆ (Fill in the stars.)

Based on the information above, decide the title of your review. _____

2 Writing: Using the information above, write your review in Japanese.

Checklist	
✓	Write horizontally from left to right and use appropriate punctuations.
✓	Write at least five sentences.
✓	Use as many grammar points as possible from the box below.
✓	Use as many learned kanji as possible.
✓	If you don't know how to spell a proper name in katakana, try writing it in katakana and provide a translation above it.

☐ Numbers and counters   ☐ Conjunctions: それから／でも／だから

☐ Adjective + Noun   ☐ Adjective or noun used as predicate

☐ で [Means marker]   ☐ から [Starting point marker]   ☐ まで [Ending point marker]

Exit Check ☑

Now go back to the Kanji List for this lesson (p.66) and do the exit check to see what kanji you can read and write.

Punctuation marks in Japanese

Does Japanese have punctuation marks like periods and commas in English?

Yes, it does! You'll find other symbols used in Japanese writing as well. Here, we'll briefly go over the use of punctuation marks for beginner level writing. Look at the examples below, and use them as a guide in your own writing!

1. Japanese punctuation marks and other symbols in common with English

English symbols	Period .	Comma ,	Quotation mark " "
Japanese symbols	まる 。	てん 、	かぎかっこ 「　」

Symbols used in both Japanese & English
？ ！ ／ ＊ ・ ＝ － （ ） ［ ］ ｛ ｝ … 〜 ： → ↓ ↑

2. Punctuation in Japanese sentences

① one character space　② bottom right of text　③ bottom right of text

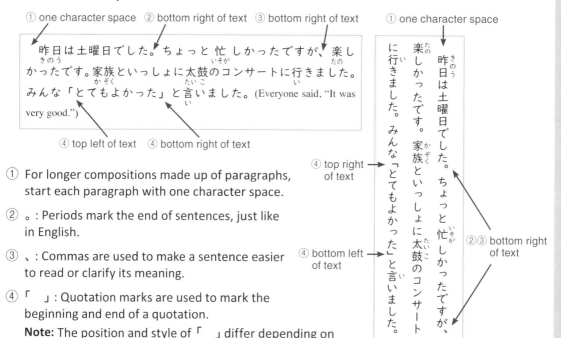

① one character space

④ top left of text　④ bottom right of text

④ top right of text

②③ bottom right of text

④ bottom left of text

① For longer compositions made up of paragraphs, start each paragraph with one character space.

② 。: Periods mark the end of sentences, just like in English.

③ 、: Commas are used to make a sentence easier to read or clarify its meaning.

④ 「　」: Quotation marks are used to mark the beginning and end of a quotation.
   Note: The position and style of 「　」 differ depending on the writing direction (horizontally or vertically).

3. Other notes

1) While Lessons 0-3 of *TOBIRA I* add spacing within sentences to make them easier for learners to read, spaces are not normally used in Japanese writing. There is no need to include spaces in your own writing.

2) Punctuation marks such as ？ and ！ are often used in casual writing, in the same way as in English. However, they are hardly ever used in more formal writing. Note that the question-marking particle か is not followed by a ？.

Writing names in Japanese

Japanese names are most often written in kanji, but hiragana and katakana can also be used. They are written with the surname first, followed by the given name. In contrast, non-Japanese names are generally written in katakana, with a "・" mark separating the given name and surname. Non-Japanese names can be written in the order of one's native language (i.e., given name first and surname second as in English).

Writing Japanese names

Ex. 赤井　圭太
あかい　けいた

surname | given name

赤井 ← surname
圭太 ← given name

Writing names in katakana

Ex. アイ・ブルーノ

given name | surname

アイ ← given name
・ブルーノ ← surname

Examples of handwriting

作文 composition
さくぶん

書道 calligraphy
しょどう

日記 diary
にっき

絵手紙 letter with a picture
えてがみ

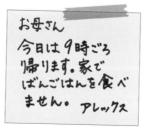

メモ note

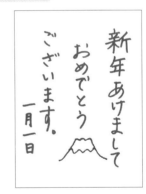

年賀状 New Year's card
ねんがじょう

手紙 letter
てがみ

Lesson 5

にゃんたがいません。
Nyanta is missing!

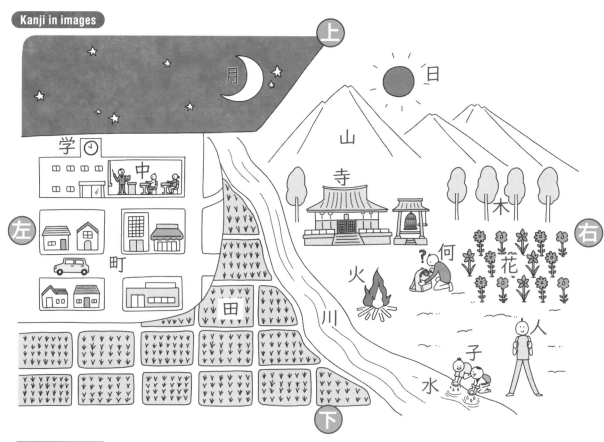

Kanji List　できるCheck ☑

	32	33	34	35	36	37	38	39	40	41	42	43	44	45	46	47	48	49
Kanji	上	下	中	外	右	左	山	川	寺	何	時	間	毎	明	今	田	町	花
Entry Check																		
Exit Check																		

Kanji in images

Kanji in daily life　Which kanji can you recognize?

今月の
おすすめ！

76

かんじのれんしゅう | Kanji practice

① Trace the gray kanji first while following the given stroke order and stoke types (stop, flick, etc.), then write the kanji twice as neatly as possible.

| S=stop F=flick R=release C=curved line ↓ → =direction ◯=note ◌=space |

Lesson 5

32	33	34	35	36	37
上	下	中	外	右	左

38	39	40	41	42	43
山	川	寺	何	時	間

separate strokes

77

Class: _____   Name: _____

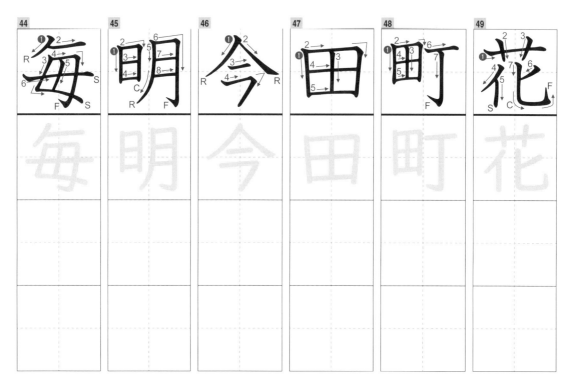

44	45	46	47	48	49
毎	明	今	田	町	花

② Make a kanji using each element and write it in the box. Then provide the meaning for each kanji in ( ).

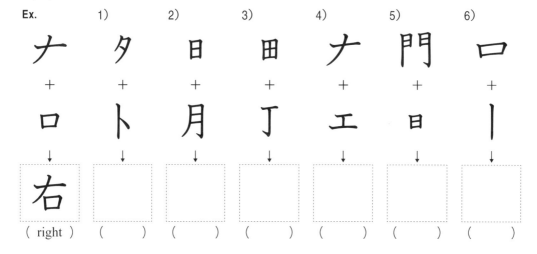

	Ex.	1)	2)	3)	4)	5)	6)
	ナ	夕	日	田	ナ	門	ロ
	+	+	+	+	+	+	+
	ロ	ト	月	丁	エ	日	｜
	↓	↓	↓	↓	↓	↓	↓
	右						
	(right)	( )	( )	( )	( )	( )	( )

③ Circle the mistake(s) in each kanji, then write the correct one in the box.

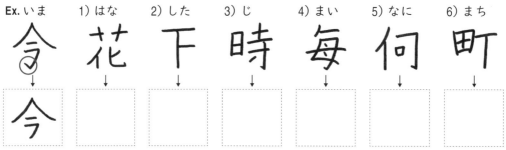

Ex. いま	1) はな	2) した	3) じ	4) まい	5) なに	6) まち
令	花	下	時	毎	何	町
↓	↓	↓	↓	↓	↓	↓
今						

④ Circle the indicated stroke in each kanji as in the example.

Ex.	1)	2)	3)	4)	5)	6)
4th	2nd	3rd	4th	1st	6th	3rd

⑤ Circle the parts in each printed kanji that differ from its handwritten version as shown in the example.

Lesson 5

Ex.	1)	2)	3)
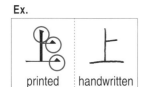	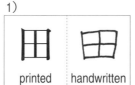		
printed handwritten	printed handwritten	printed handwritten	printed handwritten

⑥ In Japanese eye exams, you are asked to say which side of the ring is open. Determine which side is open, then write the appropriate kanji in the table as in the example.

Ex.	a.	b.
上		
c.	d.	e.
f.	g.	h.

⑦ At the vet, Nyanta got out of his cage and is running around the waiting room. Complete the conversation from the receptionist's point of view with appropriate kanji to help Ai catch him.

アイ ：あ、ケージの Ex.＿中＿ ににゃんたが

いません。

受付 ：にゃんたはケージの a.＿＿＿＿にいますよ。
うけつけ
(receptionist) あ、机の b.＿＿＿＿にジャンプしました。
つくえ

にゃんたは花の c.＿＿＿＿にいます。

あ、机の d.＿＿＿＿に入りました。
つくえ　　　　　　　　　　はい

あ、今、ソファの e.＿＿＿＿に行きました。
　　　　　　　　　　　　　　い

女の人と男の人の f.＿＿＿＿にいます。
おんな　　おとこ

あ、にゃんたは大きいイヌの g.＿＿＿＿に

行きました。
い

あ、今、テレビの h.＿＿＿＿にいます！

アイ ：えっ！　にゃんたがテレビの中に？？？

Class: _____   Name: _____

⑧ Write the reading of each date in hiragana.

Ex. 一日	a. 二日	b. 三日	c. 四日	d. 五日	e. 六日	f. 七日
ついたち						

g. 八日	h. 九日	i. 十日	j. 十四日	k. 十五日	l. 十六日	m. 十七日

n. 十八日	o. 十九日	p. 二十日	q. 何日

⑨ Below are images of some Japanese holidays and events. Answer the questions that follow in hiragana as in the example. For questions 6) and 7), write the appropriate kanji word in the boxes, then write its reading in ( ).

Ex.  1)  2)

3) 4)  5)

Ex.「昭和の日 (Showa Day)」は何月何日ですか。　　＿＿＿＿しがつにじゅうくにち＿＿＿＿です。
　　しょうわ

1)「元旦 (New Year's Day)」は何月何日ですか。　　＿＿＿＿＿＿＿＿＿＿＿＿＿＿＿です。
　　がんたん

2)「バレンタインデー」は何月何日ですか。　　＿＿＿＿＿＿＿＿＿＿＿＿＿＿＿です。

3)「子どもの日」は何月何日ですか。　　＿＿＿＿＿＿＿＿＿＿＿＿＿＿＿です。

4)「山の日」は何月何日ですか。　　＿＿＿＿＿＿＿＿＿＿＿＿＿＿＿です。

5)「文化の日 (Culture Day)」はいつですか。　　＿＿＿＿＿＿＿＿＿＿＿＿＿です。
　　ぶんか

6)（あなたの）誕生日はいつですか。　　　　　　　　　です。
　　　　たんじょうび
（Just month and day is fine.）　　　　　　（　　　　　　　　　）

7)（a major holiday/event in where you live）はいつですか。

＿＿＿＿＿＿＿の＿＿＿＿＿＿＿は　　　　　　　　　です。
place　　　　　holiday/event　　　　　（　　　　　　　　　）

80

10 Provide the kanji for the underlined hiragana words in the following sentences. The numbers in ( ) indicate the total number of kanji that should be provided.

Ex. <u>わたし</u>は<u>よにん</u>家族です。（3）
　　私　　　四人
　　　　　　かぞく

1) <u>やました</u>さんの誕生日は<u>しちがつなのか</u>です。七夕 (Star Festival) です。（6）
　　　　　a.　　　たんじょうび　　　b.　　　　　　　　　たなばた

2) 数学のクラスは<u>なんようび</u>ですか。<u>なんじ</u>からですか。（5）
　すうがく　　　　　a.　　　　　　　　b.

3) <u>たなか</u>さんはルームメートが<u>ふたり</u>います。それから、ネコが<u>ろっぴき</u>います。（5）
　　a.　　　　　　　　　　b.　　　　　　　　　　　　　　　c.

4) <u>こんげつ</u>、アニメフェアがあります。<u>そと</u>は寒いですから、建物の<u>なか</u>であります。（4）
　　a.　　　　　　　　　　　　b.　　さむ　　　　たてもの　c.

5) これは<u>わたし</u>のアニメクラブの写真です。<u>せんせい</u>は<u>がくせい</u>とがくせいの<u>あいだ</u>に
　　　a.　　　　　　　しゃしん　　b.　　　　c.　　　　　　　　d.

　います。せんせいの<u>ひだり</u>に<u>いちねんせい</u>がいます。<u>みぎ</u>に<u>よねんせい</u>がいます。（12）
　　　　　　　　　e.　　　　f.　　　　　　　g.　　h.

 11 Provide the readings for the kanji of the underlined words.

　<u>私</u>の出身は<u>上田</u>という<u>町</u>です。上田には「さくら山」という<u>山</u>があります。山の<u>上</u>に<u>古い</u>
Ex. しゅっしん　a.　　　　b.　　　　　　　　　　　　　　　　　c.　　　d.　ふる
わたし

お<u>寺</u>があります。お寺には<u>大きい</u> <u>木</u>やきれいな<u>花</u>がたくさんあります。<u>小さい</u> <u>川</u>もあります。
　e.　　　　　　　　f.　　　g.　　　　　　h.　　　　　　　　i.　　　j.

<u>子</u>どもの<u>時</u>、私は<u>毎日</u>祖父といっしょにこのお寺に<u>行</u>きました。<u>木曜日</u>には午前<u>九時</u>から
k.　　　l.　　m.　　そふ　　　　　　　　　い　　　　　n.　　　ごぜん o.

<u>十時</u>までお寺の庭 (garden) をそうじしました。それから、<u>毎年</u>、<u>十二月</u> <u>三十一日</u>の晩にお寺
p.　　　　　　　　にわ　　　　　　　　　　　　q.　　　r.　　　s.　　　　ばん

のかねをつきました (to strike a bell)。とても<u>楽</u>しかったです。お寺のかねは
　　　　　　　　　　　　　　　　　　たの

<u>今</u>もあります。
t.

　<u>大学</u>は<u>明日</u>から休みですから、<u>今日</u>の午後家に帰ります。家まで車で四時間ぐらいかかり
　u.　v.　　やす　　　　　w.　　ご ご いえ かえ　　いえ　　くるま

ます。<u>来週</u>の<u>月曜日</u>に祖父と会いますから、うれしいです。
　らいしゅう　y.　　そふ あ

 12 Referring to p.180 #5 and p.181 of *TOBIRA I*, write about your favorite place in Japanese. Use kanji that you have learned in LL3-5 as much as possible.

> **Information to include**　name and location of the place
> 　　　　　　　　　　　　thing(s), event(s), etc. the place is famous for

よむれんしゅう | Reading practice

▶See *TOBIRA I* L5 #2 (pp.182-183).

Are you interested in the Japan House and the people living there? Read Ai's composition about the Japan House and answer the questions below.

Visualizing

1） Insert the letters a.-g. into the appropriate boxes in the drawing of the Japan House below.

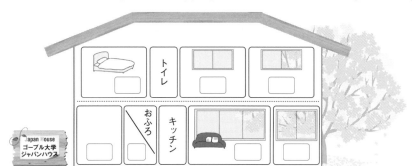

a. アイの部屋
へや

b. タオの部屋
へや

c. リーマンの部屋
へや

d. マークの部屋
へや

e. リビング

f. トイレ

g. だれもいない
(unoccupied)

2） Add simple pictures of the following things or write in the numbers ①-⑤ corresponding to them in the appropriate locations in the Japan House above.

①漢字の本　　②小さいベッド　　③大きいテーブル　　④にゃんた　　⑤小さい川
かん じ　ほん

Clarifying

3） Insert ○ into ( ) for each statement that accurately reflects the information about the Japan House.

a. (　　　) 新しい家です。
あたら　 いえ

b. (　　　) 窓から桜の木が見えます。
まど　 さくら　 き　 み

c. (　　　) 近くに鳥がいます。
ちか　 とり

d. (　　　) 近くに小さい山があります。
ちか

e. (　　　) トイレが三つあります。

f. (　　　) 近くにバス停があります。
ちか　 てい

g. (　　　) JHから大学まで自転車で二十分ぐらいです。
じ てんしゃ　 に じゅっぷん

Comprehension check

4） Mark ○ if the statement is true and ✕ if it is false.

(　　　)　JHにはメンバーが五人いますから、部屋が五つあります。
へ や

(　　　)　JHのメンバーはあまりリビングにいません。

(　　　)　にゃんたはよく小さいベッドで寝ます。
ね

(　　　)　JHでは楽しいイベントがあります。
たの

(　　　)　JHのメンバーはたいてい歩いて大学に行きます。
ある　 い

5） Answer the following question in Japanese.

ジャパンハウスでは、週末どんなイベントがありますか。
しゅうまつ

6） Would you like to live in the Japan House? Choose an option from { } and write the reason for your choice in __ to complete the sentence below.

_____から、{住みたいです／住みたくないです}。
す　　　　　　　　す
(want to live)　　　 (don't want to live)

かくれんしゅう | Writing practice

▶ Writing sheets are available on the *TOBIRA* website. (See p.6.)

Describing a room

Task: Write a composition about your room (or your dream room) in Japanese.

Ⅰ **Pre-writing activity:**

1）Draw a simple picture of your room (or your dream room).

＜**タイトル**＞（Choose one.）

☐ 私のへや

☐ 私のゆめ (dream) **のへや**

☐ other: _____

Lesson
5

2）Jot down simple keywords or phrases about the items in your room.

どこに	なにが	Description of the item / information about it
Ex. つくえのよこ	ベッド	ちょっと大きい　　ペットのイヌといっしょにねる

Ⅱ **Writing:** Using the information above, describe the room in Japanese.

Checklist	
✓	Write horizontally from left to right and use appropriate punctuations.
✓	Organize your ideas logically and write at least five sentences.
✓	Use as many grammar points as possible from the box below.
✓	Use as many learned kanji as possible.
✓	If you don't know how to spell a proper name in katakana, try writing it in katakana and provide a translation above it.

☐ X (place) に Y があります・います [Existence]

☐ X は Y (place) にあります・います [Whereabouts]

☐ X (place) で Y (event) があります [Event location]

☐ X は Y があります・います [Possession]

☐ Particle + も・は [Double particles]

☐ X という Y "Y called/named/titled X"

Exit Check ✔

> Now go back to the Kanji List for this lesson (p.76) and do the exit check to see what kanji you can read and write.

今みんなで探しています。
We are all looking for him now.

Kanji List できるCheck ☑

	50	51	52	53	54	55	56	57	58	59	60	61	62	63	64	65	66	67
Kanji	食	飲	言	話	行	来	見	持	本	語	体	口	目	耳	手	足	週	回
Entry Check																		
Exit Check																		

Kanji in images

Kanji in posters　Which kanji can you recognize?

かんじのれんしゅう | Kanji practice

★1 Trace the gray kanji first while following the given stroke order and stoke types (stop, flick, etc.), then write the kanji twice as neatly as possible.

S=stop **F**=flick **R**=release **C**=curved line ↓ → =direction ◯=note ◌=space

62	63	64	65	66	67

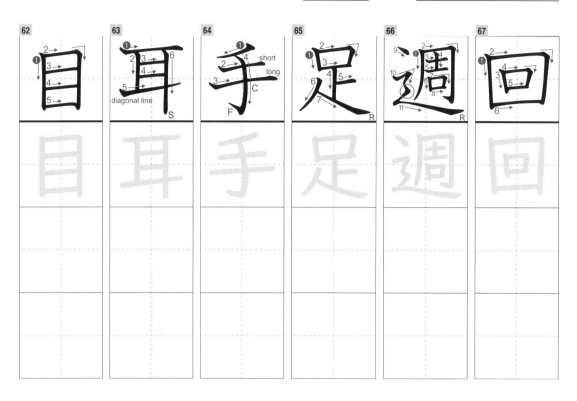

Complete the kanji 1)-9) by adding an element from the box below, then provide their readings in ( ). You may use the same element more than once.

Ex. 日 彳 亻 言 扌 飠 辶 口 止

Ex. 明	1) 欠	2) 寺	3) 吾	4) 亍
(あか)るい	(　)む	(　)つ	(　)	(　)く

5) 舌	6) 本	7) 口	8) 周 (今)	9) 口
(　)す	(　)	(　)	こん(　)	(　)

86

⭐3 Now you can write kanji for body parts, activities, etc. Write the appropriate kanji in the boxes. For kanji that indicate an action, provide *okurigana* as well.

Lesson **6**

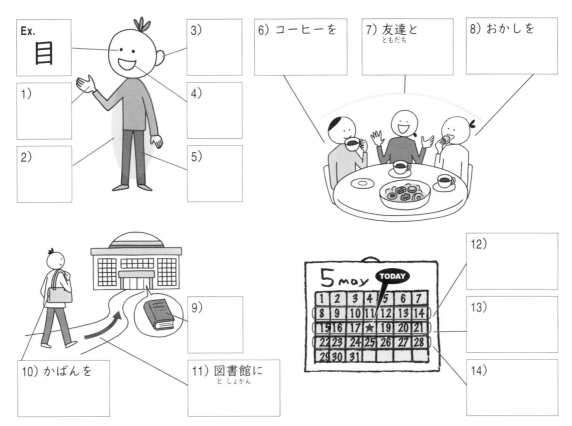

Ex. 目

3)

1)

4)

2)

5)

6) コーヒーを

7) 友達と
　ともだち

8) おかしを

9)

10) かばんを

11) 図書館に
　としょかん

12)

13)

14)

⭐4 Refer to かんじのはなし on p.198 of *TOBIRA I* and choose the correct combination of kanji and its *okurigana*.

1) 今日、カフェに ［a. 言って　b. 行って　c. 言て　d. 行て］、

　　ケーキを ［a. 食べました　b. 食ました　c. 食した］。

　　コーヒーも ［a. 飲みました　b. 飲ました　c. 飲した］。

2) 先生：日本語で ［a. 言って　b. 行って　c. 言て　d. 行て］ ください。

3) 先週の日曜日にジムに ［a. 行来ました　b. 行きました　c. 行きま下］。

4) よく友達と日本語で ［a. 語します　b. 言します　c. 話します］。
　　ともだち

5) アンさんは毎週日曜日に私のうちに ［a. 来ます　b. 木ます］。

　　アンさんは 車を ［a. 寺って　b. 持って　c. 時って］ いますから、
　　　　くるま

　　よくいっしょに買い物に行きます。
　　　　　　　か　もの

87

⭐⭐
⑤ First, write the readings of the kanji a.-h. in [ ]. Then, complete the post on social media below by choosing from a.-h. for each ( ) as in the example.

a. 一週間	b. 飲んで	c. 行って	d. 見て
[いっしゅうかん]	[ ]	[ ]	[ ]
e. 食べて	f. 二回	g. 日本語	h. 来週
[ ]	[ ]	[ ]	[ ]

1) 私は日本のアニメが好きです。^{Ex.}(a.) に (   )、見ます。
   す

2) 私も好きです！ 昨日、友達の家に (   )、いっしょに日本の
   す   きのう ともだち いえ
   アニメを (   )、話しました。

3) じゃ、(   ) の土曜日にいっしょに見ませんか。

4) いいですね。土曜日に私の家で昼ご飯を (   )、
              いえ ひる はん
   お茶を (   )、アニメを見ましょう！
   ちゃ

5) はい。それから、いっしょに (   ) を話しましょう！

⭐⭐
⑥ There is one kanji character that does not belong in each group. Circle it and choose what is in common among the others from the box below.

a. kanji element	b. body part	c. verb	d. noun

Ex. (行) 体 何　　(a.)

1) 目 足 手 回　(   )　　2) 本 耳 手 飲　(   )

3) 食 飲 本 持　(   )　　4) 口 回 語 手 足　(   )

7 Provide the kanji for the underlined hiragana words in the following sentences. Add *okurigana* as necessary. The numbers in (　) indicate the total number of kanji that should be provided.

私の好きな動物
　　　　どうぶつ

1) 私はコアラが大好きです。コアラは<u>て</u>と<u>あし</u>が短いです。それから、<u>め</u>と<u>くち</u>が
　　　　　　　だい す　　　　　　　　　a.　　b.　　　みじか　　　　　　　　　c.　　d.

　かわいいです。(4)

2) コアラは<u>からだ</u>にポケットを<u>もっ</u>ています。(2)
　　　　　　a.　　　　　　　　　b.

3) 私の国にはコアラがいません。動物園 (zoo) のコアラはオーストラリアから<u>きました</u>。
　　　くに　　　　　　　　　　どうぶつえん　　　　　　　　　　　　　　　　　　a.

　私はときどき、かわいいコアラの動画 (video) を<u>みます</u>。(2)
　　　　　　　　　　　　　　　どう が　　　　　　b.

私の日記 (diary)
　　　にっき

4) 私は<u>せんしゅう</u>の<u>どようび</u>に <u>ほんだ</u>さんといっしょに「ピース」というカフェに
　　　a.　　　　　　b.　　　　c.

　<u>いきました</u>。コーヒーを<u>のんで</u>、チーズケーキを<u>たべました</u>。(10)
　d.　　　　　　　　　　　e.　　　　　　　　　　　f.

5) ときどき、<u>にほんご</u>で<u>はなしました</u>。たくさん冗談 (jokes) を<u>いいました</u>。
　　　　　　a.　　　b.　　　　　　　　　　じょうだん　　　　　c.

　楽しかったです。(5)
　たの

6) ピースのコーヒーはとてもおいしいですから、私は<u>いっしゅうかん</u>に<u>いっかい</u>、
　　　　　　　　　　　　　　　　　　　　　　a.　　　　　　　　b.

　ピースでコーヒーを<u>のみます</u>。<u>らいしゅう</u>も<u>いきます</u>。(9)
　　　　　　　　　　c.　　　　　　d.　　　　　　e.

8 Using #7 as a model, write about your favorite animal/character or your diary. Use kanji that you have learned in LL3-6 as much as possible.

よむれんしゅう | Reading practice

▶See *TOBIRA I* L6 #2 (pp.216-217).

Pre-reading activity: Learn some new words. Match the words 1)-5) with the corresponding pictures a.-e. below.

1) 皿　　　→　ご飯の時、皿を使います (to use)。　　　(　　　)
　 さら　　　　　はん　　　さら　つか

2) きゅうり　→　緑の野菜です。　　　　　　　　(　　　)
　　　　　　　　みどり　やさい

3) 山伏　　　→　mountain priest です。着物 (traditional Japanese clothing) を着ています。　(　　　)
　 やまぶし　　　　　　　　　　　きもの　　　　　　　　　　　　　　　　き

4) 顔　　　→　顔に目と鼻と口と耳があります。　　(　　　)
　 かお　　　　かお　　　はな

5) 男の子　→　男の子どもです。　　　　　　　(　　　)
　 おとこ　　　　おとこ

a. 　b. 　c. 　d. 　e.

Reading: Now, read the passage about ようかい and answer the questions below.

Understanding Japanese sentence structure: XはYがZ

1) Underline all instances of the XはYがZ construction in the passage where it is used to describe the characteristics of various ようかい. Write your answers in your textbook.

Sorting information

2) Complete the table below in Japanese based on the information found in the passage.

Name of ようかい	Where it is found	Physical characteristics	Additional information
ざしきわらし		・	・
			・
かっぱ		・	・
		・	・
てんぐ		・	・
		・	・
		・	・

Comprehension check

3) Match each of the ようかい names on the right with the correct picture from a.-e.

a. 　b. 　c. 　d. 　e.

ざしきわらし（　　）

かっぱ　　　（　　）

てんぐ　　　（　　）

4) Fill in ___ below to explain which ようかい you like the most and why.

_____から、私は_____が好きです。
　　　　　　　　　　　　　　　　　　　　　　　　　　　　　　　　　す

90

かくれんしゅう | Writing practice

▶ Writing sheets are available on the *TOBIRA* website. (See p.6.)

[Describing a character]

Task: Create a ゆるキャラ® for your school, hometown, favorite city, etc. and describe its appearance and other characteristics.

● Read *TOBIRA* I Unit 2 チャレンジ #2, "Yuru-Chara® contest" (p.254) as a reference.

① **Pre-writing activity:** Brainstorm your ideas and create an outline.

Character's name: _____   Character for _____

Portrait

Appearance (physical traits, clothing, etc.):

Other characteristics (home, personality, hobbies, etc.):

Likes/dislikes:

② **Writing:** Using the ideas you have brainstormed above, write about your ゆるキャラ. Then, share it with your classmates.

Checklist	
✓	Organize your ideas into a paragraph consisting of at least five sentences.
✓	Describe the character (name, what they look like, where they live, hobbies, likes/dislikes, etc.).
✓	Use as many grammar points as possible from the box below.
✓	Use as many learned kanji as possible.

☐ *Te*-forms of verbs ☐ V₁ て V₂ ☐ 〜ています
☐ X は Y が Z ☐ X (period of time) に Y (number of times/duration)
☐ もう "already" and まだ "(not) yet"

Exit Check ✔

Now go back to the Kanji List for this lesson (p.84) and do the exit check to see what kanji you can read and write.

Kanji List できるCheck ✔

E = element kanji
These kanji are often used in other kanji as elements.

	68	69	70	71	72	73	74	75	76	77	78	79	80	81	82 (E1)	83 (E2)	84 (E3)	85 (E4)
Kanji	会	聞	読	立	住	知	入	売	買	物	音	楽	海	国	門	矢	貝	牛
Entry Check																		
Exit Check																		

Introduction to kanji elements 12 elements that appear in this lesson's kanji

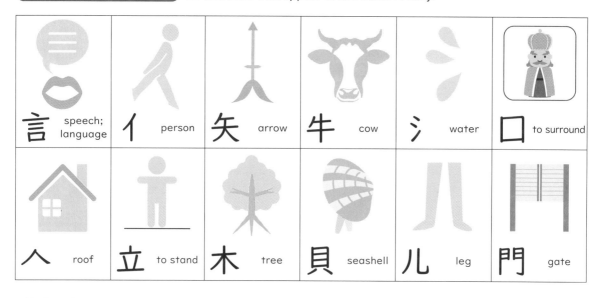

言 speech; language   イ person   矢 arrow   牛 cow   シ water   囗 to surround

入 roof   立 to stand   木 tree   貝 seashell   儿 leg   門 gate

Kanji in daily life Which kanji can you recognize?

「海の日」を
楽しもう！

どこ行く？
お出かけ特集

立入禁止
はいらないでね

売り切れ
です…

会いたい
会いたい

読みました

聞いて〜

知ってますよ

スタンプ

ピアノ & フルート
音楽教室

買い物カゴに
入れる

かんじのれんしゅう | Kanji practice

★① Trace the gray kanji first while following the given stroke order and stoke types (stop, flick, etc.), then write the kanji twice as neatly as possible.

Lesson 7

S=stop F=flick R=release C=curved line ↓→=direction ◯=note ◌=space

68	69	70	71	72	73
会	聞	読	立	住	知

74	75	76	77	78	79
入	売	買	物	音	楽

93

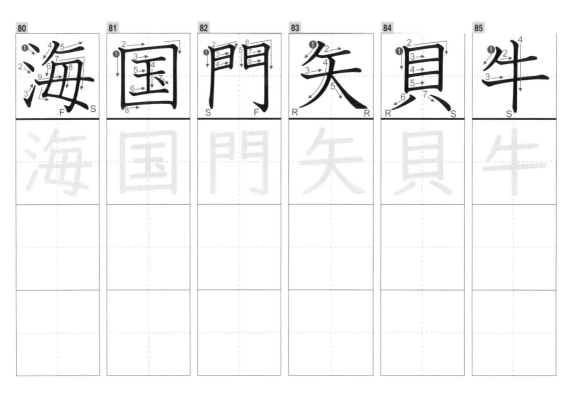

80	81	82	83	84	85
海	国	門	矢	貝	牛

2 Sort the kanji you've learned in this lesson into four groups according to their element structure and write them in the correct boxes.

会　聞　読　住　知　売　買　物　音　楽　海　国

1)

2)

3)

4)

3 Make kanji by combining one element each from A and B below, then write their meanings in ( ) as in the example. Add *okurigana* as necessary.

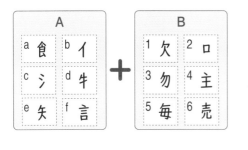

A	
a 食	b イ
c シ	d 牜
e 矢	f 言

+

B	
1 欠	2 口
3 勿	4 主
5 毎	6 売

Ex.1 <u> a </u> + <u> 1 </u> → <u>　飲（む）　</u> (to drink)

1) ___ + ___ → _____ (　　　　　)

2) ___ + ___ → _____ (　　　　　)

3) ___ + ___ → _____ (　　　　　)

4) ___ + ___ → _____ (　　　　　)

5) ___ + ___ → _____ (　　　　　)

A g 人 h 土 i 立 j 口 k 氵

+

B 7 日 8 木 9 云 10 元 11 貝

Ex.2 ___h___ + ___10___ → ___売（る）___ (to sell)

6) ___ + ___ → _____ (   )

7) ___ + ___ → _____ (   )

8) ___ + ___ → _____ (   )

9) ___ + ___ → _____ (   )

★4 Choose the correct combination of kanji and its *okurigana*.

1) [a. 聞ます   b. 聞えます   c. 聞こえます]

2) [a. 入ます   b. 入ります   c. 入いります]

3) [a. 住ます   b. 住でいます   c. 住んでいます]

4) [a. 読す   b. 読ます   c. 読みます]

5) [a. 知ます   b. 知ています   c. 知っています]

6) [a. 楽い   b. 楽しい   c. 楽のしい]

★5 Provide the readings for the kanji of the underlined words.

今年の目標 (goals for this year)
もくひょう

1) おもしろい人にたくさん会います。

2) いい本をたくさん読みます。

3) 楽しいクラブに入ります。
　　a.　　　　　　b.

4) 日本の音楽をあまり知りませんから、もっと J-POP を聞きます。
　　　　a.　　　　　b.　　　　　　　　　　　　　c.

5) 夏休みにアジア (Asia) の国に行きます。海にも行きます。
　なつやす　　　　　　　　　a.　　　　　b.

6) 友達といっしょにアパートに住みます。
　ともだち

7) 古い服を売ります。新しい物を買いません。
　ふる　ふく　a.　　　あたら　b.　c.

8) 体のために (for) バスで座りません。立っています。
　　　　　　　　　　　すわ

Class: _____   Name: _____

★
6 Look at the pictures below and describe what these people are doing by providing the appropriate words in kanji. Conjugate the verbs as necessary.

みんな、今
何をしていますか

Ex. アイスクリームを ＿＿食べて＿＿ います。

1) 店で＿＿＿＿＿＿＿をしています。
   みせ

2) フリーマーケットで服を＿＿＿＿＿＿＿います。
   ふく

3) ＿＿＿＿＿＿＿で泳いでいます。
   およ

4) おふろに＿＿＿＿＿＿＿います。

みんな、今
何をしていますか

れきし

5) ＿＿＿＿＿＿＿を楽しんでいます (to enjoy)。
   たの

6) 友達に＿＿＿＿＿＿＿て、＿＿＿＿＿＿＿います。
   ともだち　　a. (to meet)　　　b.

7) 日本の歴史を＿＿＿＿＿＿＿たいですから、歴史のまんがを＿＿＿＿＿＿＿います。
   れきし　　a. (to know)　　　　　　れきし　　　　　　　　b.

8) きれいな鳥の声が＿＿＿＿＿＿＿ますから、＿＿＿＿＿＿＿います。
   とり　こえ　　　　a.　　　　　　　　b.

9) 色々な＿＿＿＿＿＿＿の人といっしょに働いています。
   いろいろ　　　　　　　　　　　　　　はたら

★★
7 Provide the readings for the kanji of the underlined words, paying attention to the different *on*- and *kun*-readings.

Ex. 今、私のスケジュールを見ています。今月は忙しいです。
　　a. いま　　　　　　　　　　　　　　　　b. こんげつ　　いそが

1) 音楽は楽しいです。私はピアノの音が好きです。
   a.　b.　　　　　　　　　　　　c.　す

2) 中国はアジアの国です。
   a.　　　　　　　b.

3) この大学は大きい大学です。
   a.　b.

4) 来月有名な人が大学に来て、話します。
   a.　ゆうめい　　　　　　　　b.

5) 子どもの時、毎日十時に寝ました。
   a.　　　b.　ね

6) 水曜日にジョギングをして、水をたくさん飲みました。
   a.　　　　　　　　　　　　b.

7) 今、時間がありますか。銀行とコンビニの間にいいカフェがありますから、行きませんか。
   a.　　　　　　　　　　ぎんこう　　　　b.

★★
⑧ Choose the most appropriate word from a.-d. to complete each sentence, then write its reading in the space provided.

Ex. 旅行のおみやげのチョコレートです。＿＿＿たべて＿＿＿ください。
りょこう
ⓐ.食べて　　　　b. 飲んで　　　　c. 持って　　　　d. 売って

1) 私は今年、大学に＿＿＿＿＿＿＿。
a. 行きました　　b. 知りました　　c. 住みました　　d. 入りました

2) 授業 の後で、クラスメートと＿＿＿＿＿＿、日本語を話します。
じゅぎょう　あと
a. 会って　　　　b. 知って　　　　c. 買って　　　　d. 見て

3) 休みによく＿＿＿＿＿＿＿に行って、サーフィンをします。
やす
a. 山　　　　　　b 川　　　　　　c. 海　　　　　　d. 水

4) 授業 の後で、スーパーに行って、＿＿＿＿＿＿と＿＿＿＿＿＿を買いました。
じゅぎょう　あと
a. 買い物　　　　b. 食べ物　　　　c. 飲み物　　　　d. 読み物

5) 私の友達は花の名前をよく＿＿＿＿＿＿＿。
ともだち　　なまえ
a. 売っています　　b. 知っています　　c. 買っています　　d. 入っています

★★
⑨ Provide the kanji for the underlined hiragana words in the following sentences. Add *okurigana* as necessary. The numbers in ( ) indicate the total number of kanji that should be provided.

あるイヌの日記 (A dog's diary)
にっき

1) きょうはいいひでした。近くのうみにいって、波 (wave) のおとをききました。(7)
　a.　　　　　b.　　　　ちか　　c.　d.　　　　なみ　　　　e.　f.

2) ちょっとみずのなかにもはいって、遊びました。たのしかったです。(4)
　　　　　a.　b.　　c.　　　あそ　　　　d.

3) 店で色々なたべものやのみものをうっていて、みんながかっていました。そこで友達の
みせ　いろいろ　a.　　　　b.　　　　c.　　　　　　　　d.　　　　　　　　ともだち

イヌにあって、ちゅうごくのおかしをもらいました。(9)
　　　e.　　　f.

4) ここにはだいがくせいがさんにん すんでいます。晩ご飯の後で、わたしのまえにたって、
　　　　　a.　　　　　　b.　　　c.　　　　　ばん はん　あと　　d.　　e.　　f.

はなしていましたから、きいていました。(11)
g.　　　　　　　　　　　h.

5) みんなの名前はしりません。でも、まいにちおもしろいです。(3)
　　　　なまえ　a.　　　　　　b.

★★★
⑩ Using #9 as a model, write a diary entry of your day or your pet's day from their viewpoint. Use kanji that you have learned in LL3-7 as much as possible.

よむれんしゅう | Reading practice

▶See *TOBIRA I* L7 #2 (pp.251-252).

Read the essay about gift-giving customs in Japan and answer the questions below.

Sorting information

1) Complete the figures below illustrating who gives what to whom in Japan on the following occasions. Fill in ☐ under the givers and receivers with the appropriate letters a.-i. from the box below, then write what is given as a gift in ( ). There can be more than one answer.

a. 結婚する人 けっこん	b. 家族 かぞく	c. 親せき しん	d. 友達 ともだち	e. 会社の人 かいしゃ
f. 男の人 おとこ	g. 女の人 おんな	h. 子ども	i. 近所の人 きんじょ	

お正月
しょうがつ

(　　　)

前の
まえ
バレンタインデー

(　　　)

Ex. 結婚の時
けっこん

結婚おめでとう
けっこん
ございます。

a.

（お金やプレゼント）

引っこしの時
ひ

となりに
引っこししました。
ひ

(　　　)

旅行の時
りょこう

旅行に
りょこう
行きました。

(　　　)

Understanding Japanese sentence structure: あげる, くれる, and もらう

2) Who is the subject of each of the underlined verbs in the essay (reproduced below)? That is, who is the giver or receiver, depending on the verb? Choose between a. or b. and write your answers in Japanese.

　　a) l.5 <u>もらいます</u>：　　　　b) l.11 <u>あげます</u>：　　　　c) l.18 <u>くれました</u>：

　　　[a. giver　b. receiver]　　　　[a. giver　b. receiver]　　　　[a. giver　b. receiver]

Comprehension check

3) Mark ○ if the statement is true and × if it is false.

(　　　) この人 (= writer) は子どもの時、お金がほしかったですから、お正月に親せきの人に
しょうがつ　しん
会いたかったです。

(　　　) 今、日本ではバレンタインデーに女の人は何ももらいません。
おんな

(　　　) この人は結婚する人にたいていお金をあげます。
けっこん

(　　　) 牛田さんの引っこしの日、この人は牛田さんに「ありがとう」の小さいプレゼント
うしだ　　ひ　　　　　　　　　　うしだ
をもらいました。

(　　　) 旅行の時、この人のお母さんはたくさんおみやげを買いました。
りょこう　　　　　　　　かあ

4) あなたは日本のどのプレゼントの習慣が好きですか。どうしてですか。
しゅうかん　す

かくれんしゅう | Writing practice

▶Writing sheets are available on the *TOBIRA* website. (See p.6.)

Lesson
7

Gift-giving customs

Task: Write a column for a Japanese website to introduce gift-giving customs（プレゼントの習慣）
in your culture or in a country you are familiar with.
しゅうかん

① **Pre-writing activity:** Brainstorm your ideas and create an outline.

Possible topics

Pick one topic.

_____ の
(country/region)

_____ は
(custom)

☐ おもしろい

☐ ユニーク
(unique)

☐ 楽しい

☐ _____
your own

あげます

In general

　いつ　　：

　だれが　：

　だれに　：

　何を　　：

In your case

　私 {は／も}…

Other interesting
fact(s)/information

Title

② **Writing:** Using the ideas you have brainstormed above, write a short passage describing the gift-giving
customs of your choice.

Checklist	
✓	Organize your ideas into a paragraph consisting of at least six sentences.
✓	Include an opening sentence(s) to introduce the topic, a body to provide examples and details, and a closing sentence.
✓	Use as many grammar points as possible from the box below.
✓	Use as many learned kanji as possible.

☐ X という Y　　☐ *Te*-forms of verbs　　☐ *Te*-form of *i*-adjectives and です　　☐ ほしい
☐ 何か／何も〜ない　　☐ あげる／くれる／もらう　　☐ V-*masu* たい　　☐ 〜てみる

Exit Check ☑

　　**Now go back to the Kanji List for this lesson (p.92) and do the exit check to see
　　what kanji you can read and write.**

About kanji elements

Below are some common kanji elements grouped by their position within a kanji. (See かんじの
はなし on pp.229, 270, and 308 of *TOBIRA I* for more information.)

1. Left side of kanji

Element & meaning	Etymology	Kanji with this element and their meaning		Note
イ person	イ → 刃 → 人 → イ original kanji	作（る）：to make 休（む）：to (take a) rest 住（む）：to live (in place)	何 ：what 体 ：body 使（う）：to use	○　×　× イ　イ　イ
食 to eat	▲ → 食 → 食 → 食 original kanji	飲（む）：to drink （～）館：building	（ご）飯：meal; rice	element　kanji 食　食
日 sun	☀ → 日 → 日 → 日 original kanji	曜 ：day of the week 明（るい）：bright 暗（い）：dark	時 ：time 晴（れ）：sunny	element　kanji 日　日 thinner
氵 water	〜 → 氵 → 水 → 氵 original kanji	海 ：sea; ocean 消（える）：to disappear 消（す）：to turn off	洗（う）：to wash 港 ：harbor 泣（く）：to cry	○　× 氵　シ
女 woman	👤 → 女 → 女 original kanji	好（き）：to like 妹 ：younger sister 始（める/まる）：to start	姉 ：older sister 婚 ：marriage	element　kanji 女　女 thinner and angled to upper right
扌 hand	✋ → 扌 → 手 → 扌 original kanji	持（つ）：to hold	拾（う）：to pick up	element　kanji 扌　手

2. Top of kanji

Element & meaning	Etymology	Kanji with this element and their meaning		Note
雨 rain	☁ → 雨 → 雨 → 雨	雪 ：snow 雲 ：cloud	電 ：electricity 雷 ：thunder	element　kanji 雨　雨
宀 roof; house	🏠 → 🏠 → 宀	安 ：safe; 安（い）：cheap 家 ：house 寒（い）：cold	室 ：room	element　katakana 宀　ウ
艹 grass	🌱 → 🌱 → 艹	花 ：flower 英 ：English	薬 ：medicine 茶 ：tea	○　× 艹　艹

3. Bottom of kanji

Element & meaning	Etymology	Kanji with this element and their meaning	Note
儿 leg	＜image＞ → 儿 → 儿	兄：older brother　元：origin あに　　　　　　　　　げん 先：previous せん	○ 儿　　× ル

4. Upper left of kanji

Element & meaning	Etymology	Kanji with this element and their meaning	Note
广 roof	＜image＞ → 广 → 广	店：shop　　　広（い）：wide みせ　　　　　　ひろ 度：degrees ど	○ 广　　× 广
疒 sickness	＜image＞ → 疒 → 疒	病：sickness　　痛（い）：painful びょう　　　　　　いた 疲（れる）：to get tired つか	○ 疒　　× 疒

5. Lower left of kanji

Element & meaning	Etymology	Kanji with this element and their meaning	Note
辶 to walk	＜image＞ → 辶 → 辶	週：week　　　道：road しゅう　　　　みち 達：accomplished たち	○ 辶　　× 辶

6. Enclosure

Element & meaning	Etymology	Kanji with this element and their meaning	Note
囗 to surround	＜image＞ → 囗	四：four　　　　回：… times よん　　　　　　かい 国：country くに 困（る）：to have a hard time こま	This element has three strokes.
匚 to store	＜image＞ → 匚	医：doctor; medicine い 匹：[counter for small animals] ひき	This element has two strokes.
門 gate	＜image＞ → 門 → 門	間：between　　　聞（く）：to listen あいだ　　　　　　き 開（ける/く）：to open あ 閉（める/まる）：to close し	○ 門　　× 門

101

Kanji List　できるCheck ✔

	86	87	88	89	90	91	92	93	94	95	96	97	98	99	100	101	102	103
Kanji	男	女	好	作	出	書	分	午	前	後	有	名	父	母	兄	弟	姉	妹
Entry Check																		
Exit Check																		

Kanji in images

Kanji in daily life　Which kanji can you recognize?

かんじのれんしゅう｜Kanji practice

① Trace the gray kanji first while following the given stroke order and stoke types (stop, flick, etc.), then write the kanji twice as neatly as possible.

S=stop F=flick R=release C=curved line ↓ → =direction ◯=note ⬭=space

Lesson **8**

86 男	87 女	88 好	89 作	90 出	91 書

92 分	93 午	94 前	95 後	96 有	97 名

103

Complete the kanji 1)-10) by adding an element from the box below, then provide their readings in ( ). You may use the same element more than once.

曰 日 儿 口 丷 カ イ 彳 女

1) 畫 ( ) く	2) 刖 ( )	3) ロ ( )	4) タ（前） ( ) まえ	5) 罒 ( )
6) 市 ( )	7) 子 ( ) き	8) 彡 ( ) ろ	9) 乍 ( ) る	10) 未 ( )

Circle the mistake(s) in each kanji, then write the correct one in the box.

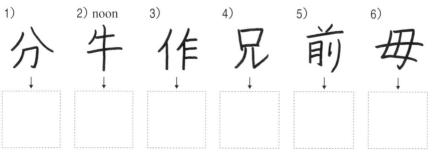

1) 分 ↓   2) noon 牛 ↓   3) 作 ↓   4) 兄 ↓   5) 前 ↓   6) 毋 ↓

4 First, write the kanji for family members to complete the family tree below. Then, draw your family tree or that of a character, using simple pictures and the kanji. If you describe a family of an anime or game character, write from their perspective.

5 Choose the appropriate reading for each underlined word from the choices in [ ].

1) 女の人　[a. おな b. おんな c. おなん] のひと　2) お父さん [a. おと b. おとう c. おとお] さん

3) お母さん [a. おか b. おかあ c. おかっ] さん　4) お兄さん [a. おに b. おにい c. おにえ] さん

5) 弟　　　[a. おとと b. おとうと c. おとおと]　6) お姉さん [a. おね b. おねい c. おねえ] さん

7) 妹　　　[a. いもと b. いもうと c. いもおと]

8) 有名な人 [a. ゆめ b. ゆめい c. ゆうめえ d. ゆうめい] なひと

6 You are communicating with your friends on social media in Japanese. Fill in each __ with the appropriate kanji word. Conjugate the verbs as necessary.

★★
7 Read かんじのはなし on p.270 of *TOBIRA I* and complete the table below with the kanji you have learned in LL6-8.

Element	Ex. イ	1) 食	2) シ	3) 女	4) イ	5) 言
Meaning of the element	person				to go; to walk around	
Kanji with this element	作					
Meaning of the kanji	to make					
Word using the kanji	作る					
Reading of the word in hiragana	つくる					

★★
8 Provide the reading for each word 1)-7), then match each word with the phrase a.-h. that explains its meaning.

	Reading	Meaning		Reading	Meaning
Ex. 学校	がっこう	a.	1) 大好き		
2) 午前			3) 兄弟		
4) 有名			5) 名前		
6) 一分			7) 出かける		

a. ここで勉強します。
べんきょう

c. すごく好きです。

e. 一人っ子にはいません。

g. 夜の12時から昼の12時までです。
よる　　　　　　　　ひる

b. みんな知っています。

d. 何かをしに外に行きます。

f. 1時5分から1時6分までです。

h. 人はみんな持っています。

★★
9 Provide the readings for the kanji of the underlined words, paying attention to the different *on*- and *kun*-readings.

1) 今週の木曜日の午前10時に作文を出します。金曜日の午後のクラスの後で、友達と
　　　　　　　　　　　a.　　　　　さくぶん　b.　　　　　　　　　　　　　　　c.　　　　　　　　　d.　　ともだち

　出かけます。いっしょに有名な美術館に行きます。美術館は公園の前にあります。
　e.　　　　　　　　　　f.　　びじゅつかん　　　　　　びじゅつかん　こうえん　g.

　歩いて五分ぐらいです。
　ある　h.

2) 私は漢字を書くのが下手です。覚えるのも苦手ですから、テストはいつも分かりません。
　　　　かんじ　　　　a.　　　　おぼ　　　にがて　　　　　　　　　　　　　　b.

3) 1930年ごろは男の人の仕事と女の人の仕事がありましたが、今はあまりありません。
　　　　　　　　a.　　しごと　b.　　しごと

4) Q: 週末、お父さんとお母さんが来る？　　A: えっと、父は来るけど、母は来ないよ。
　　　しゅうまつ　a.　　　　b.　　　　c.　　　　　　　　　　　　d.　　　　　e.　f.

5) 田中：ご兄弟がいますか。　　　　　山田：ええ、兄と弟がいます。
　　　　　　a.　　　　　　　　　　　　　　　　　　　b.　　c.

　田中：お兄さんは大学生ですか。　　山田：はい。田中さんはご兄弟がいますか。
　　　　　d.

　田中：ええ。見てください。これは姉です。大学院で外国語と文化の研究をしているから、
　　　　　　　　　　　　　　　　　　　　e.　　　　　　いん　f.　　　　ぶんか　けんきゅう

　　英語や中国語が上手です。それから、姉の後ろに妹がいます。名前はエマです。
　　えいご　　　　　g.　　　　　　　　　　　　　h.　i.　　　　　　j.

⭐⭐⭐ 10 Provide the kanji for the underlined hiragana words in the following sentences. Add *okurigana* as necessary. The numbers in (　) indicate the total number of kanji that should be provided.

私のプロフィール (profile)

1) 私は大学生です。毎日ごぜん11じからごご12じまで大学で日本語を勉強します。
　　　　　　　　　　　a.　　　　b.　c.　　　d.　　　　　　　　　　べんきょう

　クラスのあとで、よく買い物にでかけます。(8)
　　　　　e.　　　　　　　　　　　f.

2) 私は三人家族で、ははとあにがいます。イヌもいます。イヌのなまえはポチです。(4)
　　　　　かぞく　a.　　b.　　　　　　　　　　　　　　　　c.

3) はははケーキをつくるのがじょうずです。あには大学院でシェークスピアを研究して
　a.　　　　　　　b.　　　　c.　　　　　d.　　　　いん　　　　　　　　けんきゅう

　いますから、古い英語がわかります。(6)
　　　　　　ふる　えいご　e.

4) 私はよく本を読みます。『キッチン』という本がすきです。吉本ばななという人が
　　　　　　　　　　　　　　　　　　　　　　　　a.　　　　よしもと

　かきました。吉本ばななはとてもゆうめいな作家 (novelist) です。(4)
　b.　　　　よしもと　　　　　　c.　　　　さっか

⭐⭐⭐ 11 Using #10 as a model, write your own profile. When talking about family, you may also write about the family of your favorite character. Use kanji that you have learned in LL3-8 as much as possible.

Class: _____ Name: _____

よむれんしゅう | Reading practice

▶ See *TOBIRA I* L8 #3 (p.295).

1 Read the email below and answer the questions that follow.

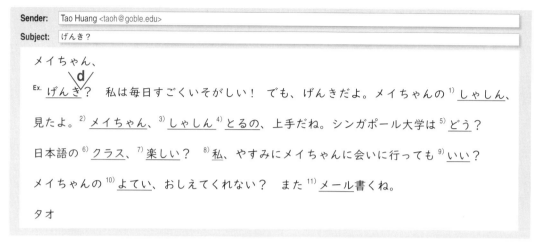

| Sender: | Tao Huang <taoh@goble.edu> |
| Subject: | げんき？ |

メイちゃん、

Ex. <ins>げん き</ins>？^d　私は毎日すごくいそがしい！　でも、げんきだよ。メイちゃんの ¹⁾ <u>しゃしん</u>、

見たよ。²⁾ <u>メイちゃん</u>、³⁾ <u>しゃしん</u> ⁴⁾ <u>とる</u>の、上手だね。シンガポール大学は ⁵⁾ <u>どう</u>？

日本語の ⁶⁾ <u>クラス</u>、⁷⁾ <u>楽しい</u>？　⁸⁾ <u>私</u>、やすみにメイちゃんに会いに行っても ⁹⁾ <u>いい</u>？

メイちゃんの ¹⁰⁾ <u>よてい</u>、おしえてくれない？　また ¹¹⁾ <u>メール</u>書くね。

タオ

Understanding the missing elements in casual expressions

1) Insert the appropriate letter from a.-d. after each of the underlined words 1)-11) to indicate the elements that would accompany those words in the polite writing style.

> a. を　　b. は　　c. が　　d. ですか

Comprehension check

2) Answer the following questions in Japanese.

a. タオさんはこのメールをだれに出しましたか。

b. その人 (that person) は、今どこにいますか。何をしていますか。

2 Read the following email Ai sent to Prof. Kuroda and fill in each ☐ with the appropriate expression from the box below.

しめきり：deadline

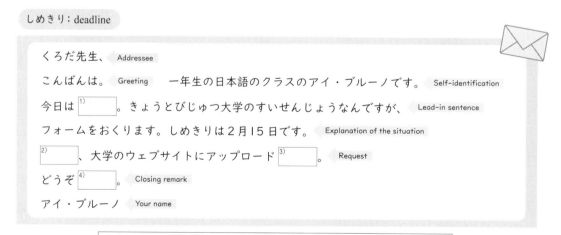

くろだ先生、 Addressee

こんばんは。 Greeting 　一年生の日本語のクラスのアイ・ブルーノです。 Self-identification

今日は ¹⁾ ☐ 。きょうとびじゅつ大学のすいせんじょうなんですが、 Lead-in sentence

フォームをおくります。しめきりは２月15日です。 Explanation of the situation

²⁾ ☐ 、大学のウェブサイトにアップロード ³⁾ ☐ 。 Request

どうぞ ⁴⁾ ☐ 。 Closing remark

アイ・ブルーノ Your name

> a. よろしくおねがいします　　b. してくださいませんか
> c. すみませんが　　　　　　　d. どうもありがとうございました

108

かくれんしゅう | Writing practice

▶ Writing sheets are available on the *TOBIRA* website. (See p.6.)

Lesson
8

Writing a formal email message

Task: Write an email message to your teacher in Japanese to ask for information or a favor.

☐ **Pre-writing activity:** Fill in the table with information to include in your email using simple keywords or phrases. (Do not write full sentences.)

Subject	
Topic	
Situation	
Reason	
Request	

② **Writing:** Referring to Ai's email message to Prof. Kuroda on p.108 #2 as a model, write your message to your teacher.

Checklist	
✓	Write the message politely, using the です・ます forms.
✓	Follow the email outline and give as much detail as you can. Insert ✓ in the box below upon including each required element in your message. ☐ Addressee ☐ Greeting ☐ Self-identification ☐ Lead-in sentence ☐ Explanation of the situation ☐ Request ☐ Closing remark ☐ Your name
✓	Use as many grammar points as possible from the box below.
✓	Use as many learned kanji as possible.

☐ X は Y が Z [Preference, skillfulness, ability]　　☐ V-plain の
☐ Place に {V-*masu*/N} に V (motion)　　☐ か [Alternative]
☐ ～んですが [Lead-in sentence ending]　　☐ ～てくださいませんか
☐ ～てもいいですか [Permission]　　☐ ～から [Reason conjunction]

Exit Check ☑

Now go back to the Kanji List for this lesson (p.102) and do the exit check to see what kanji you can read and write.

Lesson 9

すごくこわかった！
It was so scary!

Kanji List **できるCheck** ✔

	104	105	106	107	108	109	110	111	112	113	114	115	116	117	118	119	120	121 (E5)
Kanji	思	休	悪	新	古	高	校	雨	雪	晴	度	天	気	元	病	英	家	心
Entry Check																		
Exit Check																		

Kanji used in weather forecasts

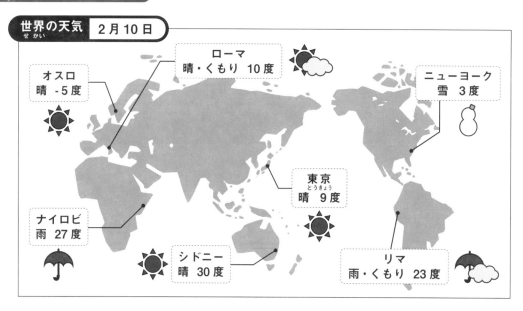

世界の天気　2月10日

オスロ　晴　-5度
ローマ　晴・くもり　10度
ニューヨーク　雪　3度
ナイロビ　雨　27度
東京　晴　9度
シドニー　晴　30度
リマ　雨・くもり　23度

Social media stickers　Which kanji can you recognize?

元気ですかー!?
いい天気だね
気分が悪い…
今日はお休みです
病気
学校
家にいる
新しい!
それ古いよ
わたしもそう思います
英語 Go! Go!

かんじのれんしゅう | Kanji practice

① Trace the gray kanji first while following the given stroke order and stoke types (stop, flick, etc.), then write the kanji twice as neatly as possible.

S=stop F=flick R=release C=curved line ↓→=direction ◯=note ⬭=space

104	105	106	107	108	109
思	休	悪	新	古	高

Lesson 9

110	111	112	113	114	115
校	雨	雪	晴	度	天

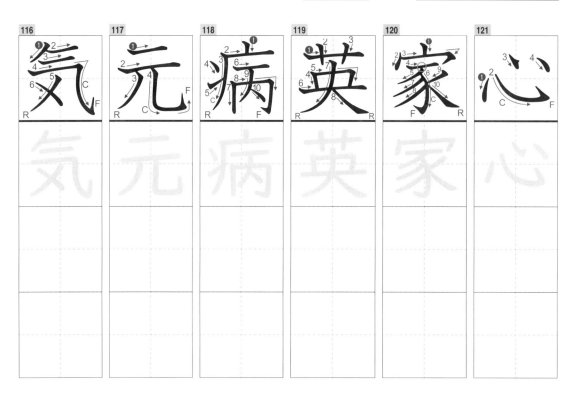

★
② Circle the parts in each printed kanji that differ from its handwritten version.

1)   2)   3)   4)

printed | handwritten

printed | handwritten

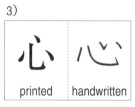

printed | handwritten

printed | handwritten

★★
③ Read かんじのはなし on p.308 of *TOBIRA I* and complete the table below with the kanji you have learned in LL6-9.

Element	1) 扌	2) 雨	3) 宀	4) 艹	5) 广	6) 疒
Meaning of the element						
Kanji with this element						
Meaning of the kanji						
Word using the kanji						
Reading of the word in hiragana						

4 Complete the kanji 1)-10) by adding an element from the box below, then provide their readings in ( ). You may use the same element more than once.

儿　心　宀　艹　日　斤　广　疒　木

1) □交 (学) がっ ( )	2) □亜 ( ) い	3) □丙 (気) ( ) き	4) □芰 (一) いち ( )	5) □二 (気) ( ) き
6) □豕 ( )	7) □青 ( ) れる	8) □央 (語) ( ) ご	9) □田 ( ) う	10) □亲 ( ) しい

5 Choose the correct combination of kanji and its *okurigana*.

1) [a. 悪るい　　　b. 悪い]　　　　　2) [a. 高かい　　　b. 高い]

3) [a. 新らしい　　b. 新しい　　c. 新い]　　4) [a. 晴れる　　b. 晴る]

5) [a. 休すみます　b. 休みます　c. 休ます]　6) [a. 思もいます　b. 思います　c. 思ます]

6 Provide the kanji or kanji compound that corresponds to each picture below. Write *okurigana* as necessary.

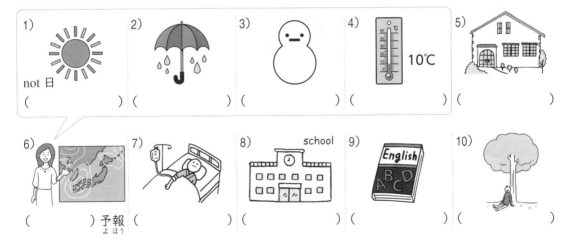

1) not 日　( )　2) ( )　3) ( )　4) 10℃ ( )　5) ( )

6) ( ) 予報
よ ほう　7) ( )　8) school ( )　9) English ( )　10) ( )

7 Provide the kanji word that has the opposite meaning of each given word below. Add *okurigana* as necessary.

Ex. 売る　⇔　____買う____　　　1) いい　⇔　_____

2) 安い　⇔　_____
やす

3) 新しい　⇔　_____

4) 晴れ　⇔　_____　　　5) 元気　⇔　_____

★★ 8 Fill in each box to make two words (for a total of 10 words) using the kanji introduced in this lesson. Each word should be read in the direction that the arrow indicates. Then, provide the reading for each word.

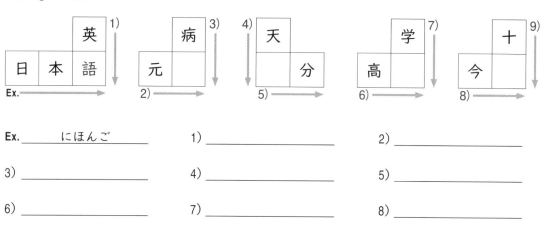

Ex.	にほんご	1)	_____	2)	_____
3)	_____	4)	_____	5)	_____
6)	_____	7)	_____	8)	_____
9)	_____				

★★ 9 Suppose you visited some festivals in Japan. Referring to p.116 of *TOBIRA I*, fill in each ___ with the appropriate kanji word.

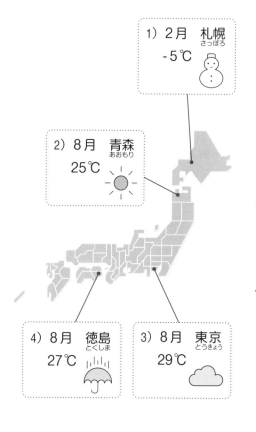

1) ２月に「さっぽろ＿＿＿＿＿まつり」に行きました。
　　　　　　　　　　　a.

天気は＿＿＿＿＿で気温はマイナス５＿＿＿＿＿でした。
　　　b.　　　　　きおん　　　　　　　　c.

2) ８月に青森の「ねぶた祭」に行きました。
　　　あおもり　　　　　　まつり

天気は＿＿＿＿＿でした。

3) ８月に東京に花火 (fireworks) を見に行きました。
　　　とうきょう　はなび

くもりで、気温は29＿＿＿＿＿でした。
　　　　　きおん

4) ８月に徳島に「阿波おどり」を見に行きました。
　　　とくしま　　あわ

＿＿＿＿＿が降って、天気が＿＿＿＿＿かったです。
a.　　　　　ふ　　　　　　　　b.

来年、もう＿＿＿＿＿行きたい
　　　　　c.

と＿＿＿＿＿ました。
　d.

⑩ Provide the kanji for the underlined hiragana words in the following sentences. Add *okurigana* as necessary. The numbers in (　) indicate the total number of kanji that should be provided.

A message to your Japanese housemate　(Suppose you live in the Japan House.)

1) 今、<u>がっこう</u>から<u>いえ</u>に帰りました。大変です！　にゃんたは<u>げんき</u>がありません。
　　　a.　　　　　　　b.　　　かえ　　　たいへん　　　　　　　　　　　　c.

　<u>びょうき</u>だと<u>おもいます</u>。（8）
　　d.　　　　　　e.

Lesson
9

A letter enclosed in a package that you sent to your friend, Tanaka-san

2) 田中さん、お<u>げんき</u>ですか。私は<u>夏</u>やすみに<u>こうこう</u>の友達といっしょに北海道に行き
　　　　　　　　a.　　　　　　　なつ　b.　　c.　　　ともだち　　　　　　ほっかいどう

　ました。田中さんに北海道のおみやげを<u>送</u>ります。（5）
　　　　　　　　　ほっかいどう　　　　おく

3) 北海道はとてもきれいでした。　<u>全然</u><u>あめ</u>が降りませんでした。　気温は 25<u>ど</u>ぐらいで、
　　ほっかいどう　　　　　　　　　ぜんぜん a.　　ふ　　　　　　　　　きおん　　　b.

　<u>毎日</u><u>はれ</u>ていましたから、いい<u>きぶん</u>でした。でも、旅館の人は「<u>冬</u>は毎日<u>てんき</u>が
　　c.　　　　　　　　　　　　d.　　　　　　　　りょかん　　　ふゆ　　　e.

　<u>わるくて</u>、<u>ゆき</u>がたくさん降るから、大変です。」と言っていました。旅館の人は全然
　f.　　　　g.　　　　　　ふ　　たいへん　　　　　　　　　　　りょかん　　　ぜんぜん

　<u>えいご</u>が分かりませんでしたから、私は日本語で話しました。（11）
　h.

4) 北海道には<u>たかい</u>山やきれいな海があります。<u>ふるい</u>建物や<u>あたらしい</u>美術館も
　　ほっかいどう　a.　　　　　　　　　　　　　　b.　　たてもの　c.　　　びじゅつかん

　あります。それから、食べ物がおいしいから、とても<u>にんき</u>があります。
　　　　　　　　　　　　　　　　　　　　　　　　　　d.

　<u>こんど</u>、田中さんといっしょに行きたいです。（7）
　　e.

⑪ Using the letter in #10 as a model, write a letter about a memorable trip you had. This could be a vacation, field trip, or smaller day trip. Use kanji that you have learned in LL3-9 as much as possible.

よむれんしゅう | Reading practice

▶See *TOBIRA I* L9 #3 (pp.332-333).

Read the article about Japanese *onsen* and answer the questions.

Visualizing

1) Suppose you are the writer of this article and are reviewing photos to be published along with it. Arrange photos a.-h. on p.332 of *TOBIRA I* in the order that the content within them appears in the article.

写真：（   ）→（   ）→（   ）→（   ）→（   ）→（   ）→（   ）→（   ）
しゃしん

Sorting information

2) Mark ◯ for the things you can do at a Japanese *onsen* and ✕ for the things you cannot.

（   ）　旅館に泊まって、畳の部屋で寝る。
　　　　　　　りょかん　と　　たたみ　へや　ね
（   ）　露天風呂に入る。
　　　　　　　ろてんぶろ
（   ）　ゆかたを着て、おいしい料理を食べる。
　　　　　　　　　　　き　　　　　　　りょうり
（   ）　木の上からジャンプして、温泉に入る。
　　　　　　　　　　　　　　　　　　　おんせん
（   ）　カピバラといっしょに温泉に入る。
　　　　　　　　　　　　　　　　　おんせん
（   ）　日本のおふろの文化を知る。
　　　　　　　　　　　　ぶんか

Comprehension check

3) Mark ◯ if the statement is true and ✕ if it is false.

（   ）　日本には火山がある。
　　　　　　　　　　か ざん
（   ）　温泉の旅館にはたいてい外におふろがある。
　　　　　　　おんせん　りょかん
（   ）　子どものサルは、寒い日には温泉に入りに来ない。
　　　　　　　　　　　　　　　さむ　　　　おんせん
（   ）　色々な動物も温泉に入るのが好きだ。
　　　　　　　いろいろ　どうぶつ　おんせん
（   ）　温泉は新しい日本の文化だ。
　　　　　　　おんせん　　　　　　　　ぶんか

4) Choose the most appropriate subtitle for this article from the box below.

a. 火山と温泉　b. おいしい日本料理！　c. 動物も温泉が大好き！　d. 温泉の歴史
か ざん　おんせん　　　　　　　　りょうり　　　　どうぶつ　おんせん　　　　　　おんせん　れき し

5) Answer the following questions based on what you have read in the article.

（1）記事 (article) の中で、何がおもしろかったですか。
　　き じ

（2）温泉で何をしてみたいと思いましたか。どうしてですか。
　　おんせん

_____と思いました。

_____からです。

かくれんしゅう | Writing practice

▶ Writing sheets are available on the *TOBIRA* website. (See p.6.)

Writing an article about a place

Task: For international students from Japan who are studying at your school, write your own article about a place where they can see the culture of your country or community you are familiar with.

Possible topics ▶ 大学　　町　　スポーツスタジアム　　古い建物
たてもの　　山　　川　　公園
こうえん

Lesson
9

① **Pre-writing activity:** Fill in the boxes with your ideas/thoughts for your article using simple keywords or phrases in Japanese. (Do not write full sentences.)

- A. トピックは何ですか。

- B. どこにありますか。

- C. 何が{有名／おもしろい}ですか。
  - •
  - •
  - •

記事 (article) のタイトル
きじ

D. どんな人が行きますか。
みんなそこで何をしますか。
  - •
  - •
  - •

E. 特に (especially) おすすめは
とく
何ですか。どうしてですか。
  - •
  - •
  - •

F. 最後に何が言いたいですか。
さいご
  - •
  - •
  - •

② **Writing:** Using the information above, write your article **vertically from right to left**. Organize the contents from A. to F. to make your article flow more naturally.

Checklist	
✓	Write your article vertically from right to left.
✓	Use the です・ます forms and pay attention to the usage of punctuation.
✓	Organize your ideas logically and write at least five sentences.
✓	Write a good opening. Also, draw a picture or insert a photograph in the article.
✓	Use as many grammar points as possible from the box below.
✓	Use as many learned kanji as possible.

☐ Adjective/verb そう [Impressions]　　☐ ～と思う　　☐ ～と言う　　☐ V-plain の
☐ ～たり～たりする　　☐ ～たことがある　　☐ 実は～んです (Refer to L9 "Conversation Tips," p.299.)
じつ

Exit Check ✓

Now go back to the Kanji List for this lesson (p.110) and do the exit check to see what kanji you can read and write.

Kanji List　できるCheck ✓

	122	123	124	125	126	127	128	129	130	131	132	133	134	135	136	137	138	139
Kanji	帰	使	暗	早	広	安	親	切	番	社	長	道	昔	友	達	文	化	末
Entry Check																		
Exit Check																		

Kanji T-shirts　Kanji T-shirts are popular among people from other countries. Which one do you like?

Kanji in daily life　Which kanji can you recognize?

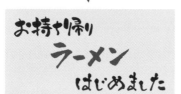

かんじのれんしゅう │ Kanji practice

★1 Trace the gray kanji first while following the given stroke order and stoke types (stop, flick, etc.), then write the kanji twice as neatly as possible.

S=stop F=flick R=release C=curved line ↓→=direction ◯=note ⬭=space

122	123	124	125	126	127
帰	使	暗	早	広	安
帰	使	暗	早	広	安

Lesson 10

128	129	130	131	132	133
親	切	番	社	長	道
親	切	番	社	長	道

129: Don't cross

119

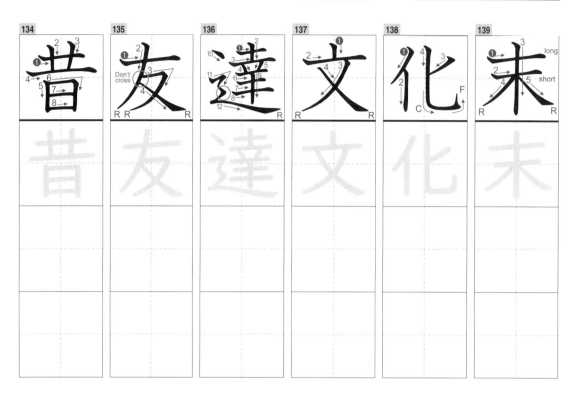

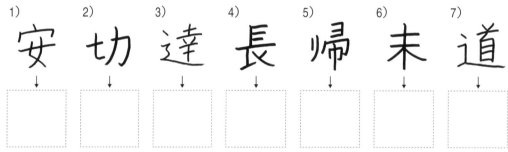

② Circle the mistake(s) in each kanji, then write the correct one in the box.

1) 安   2) 切   3) 達   4) 長   5) 帰   6) 未   7) 道

③ Make kanji by combining one element each from A and B below, then write their meanings in ( )
as in the example. Add *okurigana* as necessary.

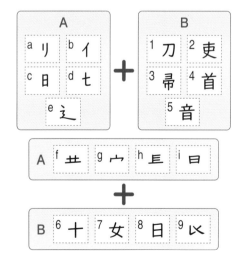

A	
a リ	b イ
c 日	d ヒ
e 辶	

+

B	
1 刀	2 吏
3 帚	4 首
5 音	

A f 甘 g 宀 h 亖 i 日

+

B 6 十 7 女 8 日 9 ㄥ

Ex. _c_ + _5_ → _暗(い)_ (dark)

1) ___ + ___ → _____ (   )

2) ___ + ___ → _____ (   )

3) ___ + ___ → _____ (   )

4) ___ + ___ → _____ (   )

5) ___ + ___ → _____ (   )

6) ___ + ___ → _____ (   )

7) ___ + ___ → _____ (   )

8) ___ + ___ → _____ (   )

4 Which of the following kanji words can go with the ending after each bracket? Circle all that apply.

Ex. [a. 読   (b.)書   (c.)聞   d. 話] きます。

1) [a. 帰   b. 切   c. 使   d. 休] ります。   2) [a. 使   b. 作   c. 安   d. 高] います。

3) [a. 暗   b. 明   c. 広   d. 長] いです。   4) [a. 親切   b. 大切   c. 昔   d. 一番] な友達です。

5) [a. 安   b. 早   c. 有名   d. 社長] くなりました。

5 Provide the kanji word that has the opposite meaning of each given word below. Then, write its reading in ( ). Add *okurigana* as necessary.

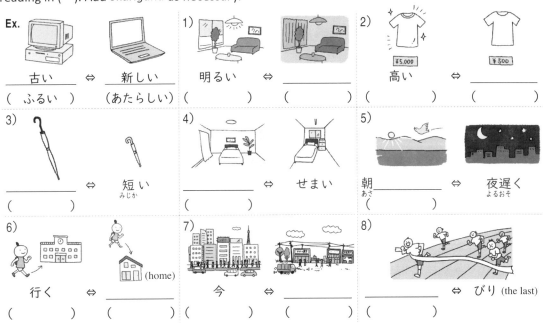

Ex.	1)	2)
古い ⇔ 新しい	明るい ⇔ _____	高い ⇔ _____
(ふるい) (あたらしい)	( ) ( )	( ) ( )

3) _____ ⇔ 短い　みじか
( )

4) _____ ⇔ せまい
( )

5) 朝_____ ⇔ 夜遅く　あさ　よるおそ
( )

6) 行く ⇔ _____ (home)
( ) ( )

7) 今 ⇔ _____
( ) ( )

8) _____ ⇔ びり (the last)
( )

6 For each sentence below, provide kanji for the words a.-c., then fill in each ( ) with the appropriate word to complete the sentence. Add *okurigana* as necessary.

Ex. 外が (c.) ですね。天気も (b.) から、(a.) でゲームをしませんか。

　　a. いえ ___家___　　　b. わるい ___悪い___　　　c. くらい ___暗い___

1) 日本の ( ) の中で、( ) に ( ) 興味があります。　きょうみ

　　a. しょどう _____　　b. ぶんか _____　　c. いちばん _____

2) 今日はバイトに行きません。家に ( ) 宿題をします。( )( ) を書きます。　しゅくだい

　　a. さくぶん _____　　b. ながい _____　　c. かえって _____

3) ( )、( ) と 湖 に遊びに行きます。朝 ( ) 出かけます。　みずうみ　あそ　　あさ

　　a. しゅうまつ _____　b. はやく _____　　c. ともだち _____

4) まず (first)、野菜を小さく ( ) ください。その野菜を ( )、おいしいサラダを　やさい　　　　　　　　　　　　　　　　　やさい
　 ( ) ください。

　　a. つかって _____　　b. つくって _____　　c. きって _____

★★ ⑦ Provide the readings for the following words. Each word should be read in the direction that the arrow indicates.

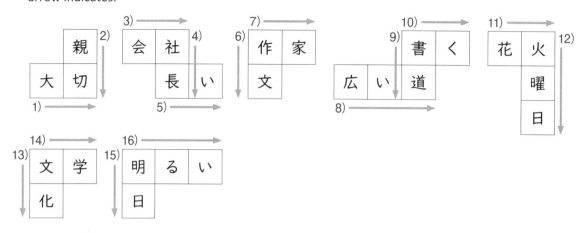

1) _____ 2) _____ 3) _____ 4) _____

5) _____ 6) _____ 7) _____ 8) _____

9) _____ 10) _____ 11) _____ 12) _____

13) _____ 14) _____ 15) _____ 16) _____

★★ ⑧ Provide the kanji for the underlined hiragana words in the following sentences. Add *okurigana* as necessary. The numbers in ( ) indicate the total number of kanji that should be provided.

> ## 10 年後 (later) の私
> ご

1) 10 年後の私は<u>ゆうめいな</u> <u>かいしゃで</u> 働 いています。<u>ひろい</u>オフィスで<u>げんき</u>で<u>しんせつな</u>
   ご   a.   b.   はたら   c.   d.   e.

   <u>しゃちょう</u>と仕事をしています。仕事では日本語も少し<u>つかいます</u>。(12)
   f.   しごと   しごと   すこ g.

2) ワークライフバランスが<u>たいせつ</u>だと<u>おもって</u>いるから、<u>ながい</u> <u>じかん</u> 働 きません。
                  a.   b.   c.   d.   はたら

   <u>くらい</u> <u>みち</u>がきらいだから、<u>はやく</u> <u>いえ</u>に<u>かえります</u>。(11)
   e.   f.   g.   h.   i.

3) <u>むかし</u>から<u>ほん</u>が<u>すきで</u>、<u>さっか</u>になりたいから、<u>しゅうまつ</u>はたいてい<u>はなし</u>を
   a.   b.   c.   d.   e.   f.

   <u>つくったり</u>、<u>かいたり</u>しています。(10)
   g.   h.

4）趣味は旅行です。日本の<u>ぶんか</u>が<u>だいすき</u>だから、<u>いちばん</u> <u>やすい</u>チケットを探して、
しゅみ　りょこう　　　　　　a.　　　　　　b.　　　　　　　　c.　　　　　d.　　　　　　　　　　さが

　　<u>いちねん</u>に<u>いっかい</u>、<u>ともだち</u>といっしょに日本に<u>いきます</u>。（14）
　　e.　　　　　f.　　　　　g.　　　　　　　　　　　　　　　h.

---

9 ★★★ Now, imagine your future. Using #8 as a model, write about your life (job, everyday life, aspirations, hobbies, etc.) 10 years from now. Use kanji that you have learned in LL3-10 as much as possible.

Lesson **10**

10 ★★★ Read かんじのはなし on p.346 of *TOBIRA I*, then create your own kanji stories as shown in the example. Share your favorite stories with your classmates.

Ex.
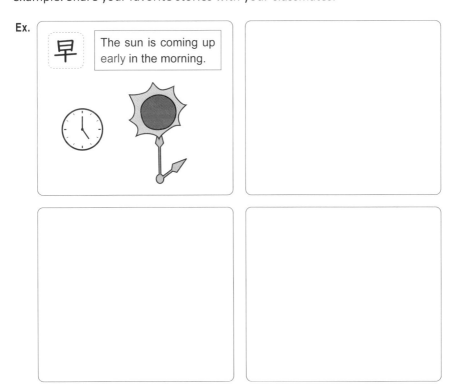

早 | The sun is coming up early in the morning.

よむれんしゅう | Reading practice

▶See *TOBIRA I* L10 #2 (pp.368-369).

『ネズミの結婚』という昔話 (old tale) を読んで、質問に答えましょう。

Understanding demonstratives (そ-words)

1）What do the そ-words (①-⑥) in the passage refer to? Underline the words or sentences and draw arrows to connect them with the そ-words which refer to them. Write your answers in your textbook.

Recognizing sequence

2）Put the story in proper chronological order. Indicate the order by writing numbers in (　) below each picture.

a. (　　　)　　　　　　b. (　　　)　　　　　　c. (　　　)

d. (　　　)　　　　　　e. (　　　)　　　　　　f. (　　　)

Comprehension check

3）Answer the following questions in Japanese.

（1）チュー子はどんなネズミですか。

（2）お父さんネズミはどうして太陽が世界で一番強いと思いましたか。

（3）チュー子はどうしてネズミと結婚しましたか。

4）What do you think かべ said to お父さんネズミ in l.26 (p.368, *TOBIRA I*) to answer his question? Write your own answer that fits in ☐ in the space provided below.

かべは「ネズミさんは＿＿＿＿＿＿＿＿＿＿＿＿＿からです。」と答えました。

かくれんしゅう | Writing practice

▶ Writing sheets are available on the *TOBIRA* website. (See p.6.)

Who is the most ...?

Task: Write your opinion by answering the question 「○○の中で、だれが {一番 Adj か／一番よく Verb か}」.

① **Pre-writing activity:** Brainstorm your ideas and create an outline. Fill in the boxes with your ideas using simple keywords or phrases in Japanese. (Do not write full sentences.)

Lesson **10**

Your opinion about the topic:

_____の中で、_____が

一番_____と思います。
(Exs. 強い, やさしい)

一番よく_____と思います。
(Ex. 本を読む)

(group of people, characters, etc.)

Reason/fact #1:	Reason/fact #2:	Reason/fact #3:

Concluding remark:

② **Writing:** Using the ideas you have brainstormed above, explain your opinion.

Checklist	
✓	Create a good title for the passage.
✓	Use the です・ます forms and pay attention to the usage of punctuation.
✓	Organize your ideas logically and write at least five sentences.
✓	Support your opinion with reasons and examples.
✓	Use as many grammar points as possible from the box below.
✓	Use as many learned kanji as possible.

□ Adverbial forms of adjectives □ ～なる／する □ Superlative sentences
□ Comparative sentences □ X も Y も □ ～ことができる
□ ～たり～たりする □ ～けれど

Exit Check ✓

Now go back to the Kanji List for this lesson (p.118) and do the exit check to see what kanji you can read and write.

	1	2	3	4	5	6	7	8	9	10
	一	二	三	四	五	六	七	八	九	十
	11	12	13	14						
L3	月	私	子	人						
	15	16	17	18	19	20	21	22	23	24
	百	千	万	円	曜	日	火	水	木	金
	25	26	27	28	29	30	31			
L4	土	学	生	先	年	大	小			
	32	33	34	35	36	37	38	39	40	41
	上	下	中	外	右	左	山	川	寺	何
	42	43	44	45	46	47	48	49		
L5	時	間	毎	明	今	田	町	花		
	50	51	52	53	54	55	56	57	58	59
	食	飲	言	話	行	来	見	持	本	語
	60	61	62	63	64	65	66	67		
L6	体	口	目	耳	手	足	週	回		
	68	69	70	71	72	73	74	75	76	77
	会	聞	読	立	住	知	入	売	買	物
	78	79	80	81	82	83	84	85		
L7	音	楽	海	国	門 (E1)	矢 (E2)	貝 (E3)	牛 (E4)		
	86	87	88	89	90	91	92	93	94	95
	男	女	好	作	出	書	分	午	前	後
	96	97	98	99	100	101	102	103		
L8	有	名	父	母	兄	弟	姉	妹		
	104	105	106	107	108	109	110	111	112	113
	思	休	悪	新	古	高	校	雨	雪	晴
	114	115	116	117	118	119	120	121		
L9	度	天	気	元	病	英	家	心 (E5)		
	122	123	124	125	126	127	128	129	130	131
	帰	使	暗	早	広	安	親	切	番	社
	132	133	134	135	136	137	138	139		
L10	長	道	昔	友	達	文	化	末		

* Kanji with "E" indicates the kanji used in many other kanji as elements, so you will encounter them frequently as you continue to study Japanese.

著者紹介

■ 岡 まゆみ • Mayumi Oka
おか

現職　ミドルベリー日本語学校日本語大学院プログラム講師
教歴　ミシガン大学アジア言語文化学科日本語学課長
　　　プリンストン大学専任講師, コロンビア大学専任講師, 上智大学講師
著書　『中・上級者のための速読の日本語 第2版』(2013);
　　　『マルチメディア日本語基本文法ワークブック』共著
　　　(2018)(以上、ジャパンタイムズ出版);『上級への
　　　とびら』(2009);『きたえよう漢字力』(2010);『中
　　　級日本語を教える教師の手引き』(2011);『これで
　　　身につく文法力』(2012);『日英共通メタファー辞
　　　典』(2017);『初級日本語 とびらⅠ』(2021));『初
　　　級日本語 とびらⅡ』(2022);『とびらⅠワークブッ
　　　ク2』(2023);『とびらⅡワークブック1』(2023)
　　　(以上共著、くろしお出版);その他
その他　全米日本語教師学会理事(2007-2010)
　　　ミシガン大学 Matthews Underclass Teaching
　　　Award(2019)

■ 近藤 純子 • Junko Kondo
こんどう じゅんこ

現職　南山大学外国人留学生別科専任語学講師
教歴　マドンナ大学非常勤講師, ミシガン大学専任講師
著書　『上級へのとびら』(2009);『きたえよう漢字力』
　　　(2010);『中級日本語を教える教師の手引き』
　　　(2011);『これで身につく文法力』(2012);『初級
　　　日本語 とびらⅠ』(2021));『初級日本語 とびらⅡ』
　　　(2022);『とびらⅠワークブック2』(2023);『と
　　　びらⅡワークブック1』(2023)(以上共著、くろし
　　　お出版)

■ 榊原 芳美 • Yoshimi Sakakibara
さかきばら よしみ

現職　ミシガン大学アジア言語文化学科専任講師
教歴　ミシガン州立大学専任講師, 北海道国際交流セン
　　　ター日本語日本文化講座夏期セミナー講師
著書　『マルチメディア日本語基本文法ワークブック』
　　　(2018)(共著、ジャパンタイムズ出版);『初級日本語
　　　とびらⅠ』(2021));『初級日本語 とびらⅡ』(2022);
　　　『とびらⅠワークブック2』(2023);『とびらⅡワー
　　　クブック1』(2023)(以上共著、くろしお出版)

■ 西村 裕代 • Hiroyo Nishimura
にしむら ひろよ

現職　イェール大学東アジア言語文学部専任講師
教歴　オバリン大学講師, オハイオ大学講師, ヴァッサー
　　　大学日本語フェロー, オレゴン大学夏期講習講師,
　　　CET Academic Program 夏期講習講師
著書　『とびらⅠワークブック2』(2023);『とびらⅡワー
　　　クブック1』(2023)(以上共著、くろしお出版)

■ 筒井 通雄 • Michio Tsutsui [監修]
つつい みちお

現職　ワシントン大学人間中心設計工学科名誉教授
教歴　コロンビア大学日本語教育夏期修士プログラム講師,
　　　ワシントン大学教授, マサチューセッツ工科大学助教
　　　授, カリフォルニア大学デービス校客員助教授
著書　『日本語基本文法辞典』(1986);『日本語文法辞典
　　　〈中級編〉』(1995);『日本語文法辞典〈上級編〉』
　　　(2008);『マルチメディア日本語基本文法ワーク
　　　ブック』(2018)(以上共著、ジャパンタイムズ出
　　　版);『上級へのとびら』(2009);『きたえよう漢字
　　　力』(2010);『中級日本語を教える教師の手引き』
　　　(2011);『これで身につく文法力』(2012);『初級
　　　日本語 とびらⅠ』(2021));『初級日本語 とびらⅡ』
　　　(2022);『とびらⅠワークブック2』(2023);『と
　　　びらⅡワークブック1』(2023)(以上共著、くろし
　　　お出版);その他
その他　全米日本語教師学会理事(1990-1993, 2009-
　　　2012)

制作協力

■ 校正・英語校正

平川ワイター永子（ひらかわ えいこ）（**Eiko Hirakawa Weyter**）
現職 フリーランス日本語教師
教歴 ミシガン大学専任講師, パデュー大学専任講師

■ 英語翻訳・校正

Robin Griffin（ロビン・グリフィン）

■ イラスト

坂木浩子
村山宇希

■ 装丁・本文デザイン

鈴木章宏

■ 編集

市川麻里子
金髙浩子

初級日本語 とびらI ワークブック 1
―ひらがな・カタカナ, かんじ, よむ, かく
TOBIRA I: Beginning Japanese　Workbook 1
―Hiragana/Katakana, Kanji, Reading, Writing

2022年 10月 7日　第1刷発行
2024年　1月16日　第2刷発行

著　者 ◉ 岡まゆみ・近藤純子・榊原芳美・西村裕代
監　修 ◉ 筒井通雄
発行人 ◉ 岡野秀夫
発行所 ◉ くろしお出版
　　　　〒102-0084　東京都千代田区二番町4-3
　　　　Tel: 03-6261-2867　　　Fax: 03-6261-2879
　　　　URL: https://www.9640.jp　Email: kurosio@9640.jp
印　刷 ◉ シナノ印刷

© 2022 Mayumi Oka, Junko Kondo, Yoshimi Sakakibara, Hiroyo Nishimura, Michio Tsutsui, and Kurosio Publishers, Printed in Japan
ISBN978-4-87424-910-9 C0081